the OVAL PLAYGROUND

William Campbell Gault

E. P. DUTTON & CO., INC.
NEW YORK

Library of Congress Catalog Card Number: 68–24721

Fifth Printing, June 1972

SBN 0–525–36525–7

FOR ELLIOTT MACRAE
Who never told me anything that was not true.

the OVAL PLAYGROUND

chapter ONE

I GUESS ALL HIGH SCHOOLS HAVE THEIR cliques. At least among the boys there are the athletes and the politicians and the social butterflies. At our school we also had the surfers and what the great Larry Beam had named the "grease balls."

Larry was the varsity quarterback, president of the senior class and a pretty smooth dancer so I suppose he could be called a three-clique man. A very popular guy—though not among the surfers or the grease balls.

I was one of the grease balls. It only meant I couldn't *always* get *all* of the grease out from under my fingernails or the pores of my knuckles. There were a couple dozen of us in the school, some with Hondas, a few with big Harleys, but most of us in the world of four wheels, either custom or rod.

Before my dad died, we lived on a ranch, so I had started taking machines apart early in life. After he died, we moved to town. Mom got a job in the library, and I worked after school at Al's Garage.

Al Duncan ran Al's Garage. He'd gone to high school with my dad and they'd been in the grease ball clique, too—Dad with a hot Chev, Al with a custom Ford. When I went to work for Al, I was driving a shell as old as the one he'd had in high school. But I had installed a blown Dodge engine in it.

It was designed for drags, but I used it on the street, too. It was my only transportation. Al's street car was an ancient classic, a thirty-five-year-old supercharged Duesenberg SJ.

So you can see, despite the scorn of Larry Beam, it wasn't a bad world I lived in, working for a man who appreciated the Duesenberg and getting paid for working on cars. And Al let the gang use the shop nights (as long as I was there), so it was kind of our second home.

It was a warm night in April of my senior year when Al asked me, "Plan to work here this summer?"

"If you don't fire me."

"How about college?" he asked.

"Not this fall. I have to stash a few more dollars first."

"I figured you might," he said. "I can work you forty hours a week here." He paused. "And if you wanted to pick up a few extra dollars, you could work on percentage Sundays."

I didn't understand him at first. "Percentage?" I

said. "Sundays?" I looked up from the engine I had been working on.

"Tom Winter wants to sell his Rafield," he explained. "Back to the dirt, back to the noisy Sundays."

I continued to stare at him. "Back?"

"Didn't your dad ever tell you about it, about the two of us?"

"He told me about a couple of summers," I said, "when you were just kids. He told me you did some dirt track racing."

"Well, that's what I'm talking about now."

"There's not much dirt left," I said. "Most of the tracks have been blacktopped. That Rafield would never make it on a fast track, dirt or hard surface."

"I'll stick to the dirt that's left. And we can soup that engine some more."

I didn't know what to say. Here he was, over forty years old, and though he'd gone to a few races in the two years I'd worked for him, he'd never once mentioned anything like this.

I continued to say nothing. He grinned at me. "Think about it. I've got to deliver a car and I'll go home from there. You can lock up."

I was still working and thinking about what he'd said when Pete Lopez came in with his Honda. Pete had gone from a competition coupe to a street roadster to a Harley and now a Honda, downhill all the way.

11

I told him about Al's summer plans.

"Dirt?" he said. "What dirt? Maybe half a dozen tracks here and there are still dirt. But no money tracks."

"Al said dirt only. But maybe he figures if we can improve the engine in that Rafield enough, he can make out on the hard tracks, too."

Pete shrugged. "He should know. He's the mechanic. He's been going to races, hasn't he?"

"A few. But he never talked about them much. This came from nowhere. It doesn't make sense!"

"Don't try to figure it, Mark," Pete said. "Don't try to figure out anybody over twenty-five."

Well, my mom's over twenty-five and I could always understand her. Of course, she goes out of her way to make things *very* clear to me. Dad had been in the Navy during the war and he had taught her to run a tight ship.

When I told her what Al had said, she smiled.

"What's he trying to prove?" I asked.

"Maybe he's trying to prove he's still seventeen years old—inside."

"What's so great about being seventeen?"

"It's hard to explain to anybody under thirty," Mom said, "but it's a kind of fever that hits us old folks every spring. Don't you worry about Al. He'll forget this nonsense as soon as we have a cold spell."

"You're not old folks, Mom."

"I'm thirty-eight."

"You could pass for thirty-seven, any time," I told her. "Is there any ice cream in the freezer?"

She looked at me steadily, saying nothing.

"Thirty?" I suggested.

No answer.

"You could pass for twenty-eight," I said. "Easily!"

"There's ice cream," she said. "Fudge ripple."

I was digging out a plate of that, when Mom said, "They'll soon be over, won't they?"

"What?"

"Your best years," she said. "The high school years—those are the best."

"They were all right," I admitted. "Were you thinking about Al?"

"No," she said. "Bring me a dish of ice cream, too, please. But not the same size. I have to watch my weight."

I brought her a medium dish and took my own giant economy size to the other side of the kitchen table.

"I wasn't thinking about Al," she went on. "I was thinking about you. You never played football, baseball or basketball. You never even went to the games. You never went to the dances or joined the glee club or the debating society."

"I've been a one-clique man," I admitted.

She frowned. "What—?"

"It's an inside joke," I explained. "It's the way Pete Lopez catalogs the guys at school—you know, athletes, surfers, politicians—"

"Pete has a sharp tongue," she said. "I suppose he looks on these people with contempt?"

I shook my head. "Never. Not Pete. Resentment, but no contempt."

Mom laughed—and then stopped. "It's not funny, is it?"

"Not to Pete, I guess. It's not easy being Mexican; it limits your cliques."

"And you?" she asked. "What limited your cliques?"

"I don't know, Mom. I just like cars. They're enough for me—I guess that's the way it is. What's wrong with that?"

She sighed. "I just have this feeling you've missed something."

I smiled.

"What's funny?" she asked.

"You and Al," I said. "Al wants to go back to those days when he and Dad toured the dirt tracks and you want to go back to the Junior Prom. I didn't miss anything, Mom. Look at the grades I brought home. What's school for?"

"Well, I suppose a librarian shouldn't say it, but school should be something more than books and grades."

"It was for me," I said. "I met Pete Lopez and Joe

14

Moreno and Red Halloran. I met a lot of great guys."

Mom shook her head impatiently. "I'm not getting through. But don't relax; I intend to keep trying."

Who needed dances and football? There was music in an engine and competition in a drag. Who needed politics? There was more challenge and ingenuity in rebuilding a clunker. And as for friends—I had the kind who talked my language. Which left only surfing, a religion I could never understand.

At school the next day, Joe Moreno asked, "What's with your boss? He's not really going to race this summer, is he?"

"He's thinking about it."

"Is he crazy?"

I shrugged.

"He's no kid!"

"Right," I agreed.

Joe smiled. "I think I've got it. But you don't want your mother to know, right? You're going to drive. You're the one with the experience."

"What experience?"

"Track and strip, both," he said.

I had driven in jalopy races at Canyon City— until Mom had found out about it. I had driven in dozens of drags. I said, "If that's what Al has in mind, he hasn't told me about it. I have a feeling he plans to do his own driving."

When I reported to work that afternoon, Tom

15

Winter's Rafield was in a corner of the garage on blocks, the wheels off.

"You bought it," I said.

"Not yet," Al said. "I'm going to check it over, first."

"And then you're going to buy it."

He grinned at me. "Shouldn't I?"

"You're the boss. I can't tell you what to do."

"You and Joe and Pete and Red," he said, "you guys act like I'm a hundred and eight years old. What's wrong with a mature man having a little fun on his day off?"

"I never thought you were a hundred and eight," I said, "and neither did the other guys. We all figured you for forty-two, which you will no longer be on July seventh. If you want to have some Sunday fun, what's wrong with drags? Why don't you build a rod?"

"It's not the same," he argued. "A quarter of a mile from a standing start—that's not racing. It's not the same!"

And neither are you, I thought. *You're twenty-five years older than your dream.*

"You know it's not the same," he insisted. "Wasn't Canyon City more fun than drag racing?"

"It wasn't run as well," I said. "It had bad management."

"I didn't ask you that."

"Okay," I admitted, "it was more fun."

16

"So there's your answer," he said.

If he didn't plan to win—only to have some fun—how could I work on percentage? It didn't seem to be the right time to ask that.

There was nothing heavy on the work sheet—a muffler to install, two tune-ups. I worked on those while Al dug into the Rafield like a kid taking a new toy apart.

I was washing up when Tom Winter came in. "Well?" he asked Al.

Al shook his head doubtfully. "It's in pretty bad shape, Tom. How long has it been stored?"

"A year and a half. You didn't find any rust, did you?"

"Some. I don't know—"

"I still have the trailer hooked onto my truck," Tom said. "I can haul it away right now. You know the price; I'm not dickering."

"Give me another day," Al suggested. "Give me until noon tomorrow."

"Okay." Tom paused. "If you should buy it, who's going to drive it for you?"

"Stick to pumping gas," Al told him. "You'll never make it as a comedian."

"I'm not trying to be funny."

"Then you've got a short memory," Al said. "I used to run you into the ground almost every time out."

Tom Winter didn't say anything for seconds. Finally, he said, "I heard it around town but I didn't believe it. You've lost your mind!"

"Maybe. We'll see."

Tom took a deep breath, glanced at me and shook his head. "Well, I'm not your keeper. I'll phone you at noon tomorrow."

He went out looking grim, but Al didn't seem to notice. He was studying his new toy. I went over to stand next to him.

"Sound chassis," he said, "but you could be right about the engine."

It was a rocker-arm four. "It's out of the stone age," I said. "Why not buy the chassis and tell him to keep his engine?"

"He'd never go for it. He's annoyed enough with me already."

"We could drop a little Chev engine in there," I suggested, "and you'd have all the horses you need for the competition you plan to meet."

He looked at me suspiciously. "What kind of crack was that? What kind of competition do you think I have in mind?"

"You said dirt track," I explained. "How many of those are left? And what runs on them? Clunkers and junkers."

"There are still a few fast dirt tracks. For your information, Andretti and Foyt raced at San Valdesto last fall. Are they running junkers?"

18

"Last I heard," I said, "they were running engines that the Ford Motor Company sells, *at a loss,* for twenty-three thousand dollars *each.*"

"Okay!" he said. "So I settle for third at San Valdesto."

I stared at him. Then he started to laugh and we were both laughing. With Al, you never knew. . . .

"Go home and eat your dinner," he said. "Maybe it'll turn cold tonight and I'll get my sanity back."

That was the thought Mom had voiced; the warm spring was to blame. But Al had driven that old Duesenberg through a few winters so he might stay just as stubbornly sentimental about this. And why not? It was his money and his neck.

Joe Moreno wanted me to help him get his coupe ready for a drag at Santa Maria so I went back to the garage after dinner.

Joe was waiting in front when I got there. "I've been hearing things around town," he told me.

"You usually do. What's the gossip this time?"

"There's a new racing league being formed, all dirt. I'll bet that's why your boss wants to buy that car."

"All dirt? A league? There aren't that many dirt tracks in California."

"It'll cover three states," Joe said. "Here, Arizona and Nevada." He smiled. "One of your old stamping grounds is going to be in it—Canyon City."

"Some league!" I said.

"It's plenty fast enough," Joe said, "for a fifty-year-old man driving that worn-out Rafield."

"Al's not fifty," I said. "He's just a kid of forty-two."

chapter TWO

THE REST OF THE TRACKS IN THE NEW Western Dirt Track Association were a step or two up from the Canyon City bull ring. Two of them, at San Valdesto and Linus, had been running USAC races for several years. They're the big boys in racing, the USAC, the boys who took over Indianapolis after the Triple-A bowed out.

That didn't make the new WDTA drivers the small boys. Sentimentalists, I guess you could call them, lovers of the dirt. They would be wheeling mounts far too fast for that Rafield and most of them would be men who had learned the trade well.

We had to find a better engine if we wanted to compete in that company. The next day was Saturday and I was at the garage when Al tried to explain that to Tom Winter. Tom evidently thought it was a gimmick to knock down his asking price. He must have started to walk out at least half a dozen times. They finally made the deal much closer to Tom's figure than to Al's. Tom was selling a white elephant and Al was buying a dream.

"And now," Al said, "I think I'll run down to San Diego tomorrow. Want to go along?"

"I can always use the air. What's in San Diego?"

"An engine. Stan Nowak's got his D-O four up for sale."

Stan Nowak's driving days were more recent than Al's. He had retired with a stiff leg after cracking up last fall. I asked, "Will you let me drive the Duesy part of the way?"

He nodded, his mind somewhere else. And then he said lightly, "Maybe your mom would like to go along."

"If she isn't working," I said. "She works one Sunday a month."

Al had gone with Mom in high school until Pop had come along with his big smile and hot Chev. Al had never married.

At home, Mom asked what I had: "What's in San Diego?"

"A D-O four," I told her.

"What's that—a horse?"

"It's a whole barnfull of horses. It's an engine with four cylinders and sixteen valves and overhead camshafts—*two* overhead camshafts. Get it—double overhead—D-O?"

"How exciting!" she said. "I can hardly wait to see it!"

I sighed. "You certainly can be sarcastic. Do you think Al's still sweet on you?"

22

"We'll find out tomorrow," she said. "We'll see what kind of dinner he buys us. Is this engine for his truck?"

"Nope. It's for his new racing car."

"He's done it!" she said. "That crazy man has gone and bought that contraption of Tom Winter's."

I nodded.

"Now, why? Could you tell me why?"

I shrugged. "I guess the cold spell didn't come in time. Don't bug him about it tomorrow. He's a big boy now."

"Boy," she agreed, "that's the right word. Well, I suppose it's none of my business."

She didn't sound as if she meant it. Bringing up a red-blooded son like yours truly had given Mom certain hardened attitudes about proper male behavior and she'd known Al a lot longer than she'd known me. He was *family,* in a way.

He pulled up in front of the house about nine the next morning, his shoes as shiny as the Duesenberg, wearing a whole new and bright set of threads. In cars and clothes, Al bought only the best. He had a small trailer hitched on the back so he must have been half sold on the engine already.

Mom was wearing the new dress she'd bought in San Francisco when she'd gone up to the librarians' convention. She could have passed for thirty-six, easily.

Outside of the shop, Al worked to wider toler-

23

ances than I did. He told Mom, "You don't look a day over sixteen."

"And you don't act it," she said. "What's the trailer for?"

"I might do a little business while I'm down there," he said stiffly. "Should we eat at the Presidio Sky Room?"

"If you have any money left after you finish your *business*," Mom said. "That's a very expensive restaurant."

"Now, Elly—" he said. He shook his head and looked at me. He took a deep breath and said evenly, "It's a nice day and it should be a nice trip. Let's not spoil it before it's started."

"Okay," Mom said. She smiled at both of us. "Away we go!"

It was a nice trip, going down. Mom can be fun when she's not involved in some disciplinary problem, and the ocean was blue instead of gray, for a change. It was in sight most of the way. And when we got to Stan Nowak's Midtown Garage—well, *there* was a place more impressive than the Pacific.

It was big, well lighted, airy, tooled to the minute. As a driver, Stan had campaigned on the dirt. As an owner, designer and pit mechanic, he'd had cars in the first ten at Indy for three consecutive years.

"I hope you came prepared to buy without stalling," he told Al. "I usually play golf on Sundays."

"If the price is right and it'll fit Tom Winter's

24

chassis," Al said, "this shouldn't take long. Where is it?"

"It'll fit Tom's chassis," Stan said. "You already know the price. It's over here, crated and ready to go."

It was in the Miller, Offy, Meyer-Drake tradition, the big four. But the block had been cast in Fontana and the rest was all Nowak. You can't copyright specs.

Al stared at it, his hunger in his eyes.

"Well?" Stan asked. "I can still catch the rest of the foursome before they tee off."

"I guess," Al said. "Do you have enough men around to load it for me?"

Stan nodded.

"I'll leave the trailer here," Al said. "I thought we'd run over to Coronado for the afternoon and then have dinner at the Presidio before we head back."

"Fair enough," Stan agreed. "It'll be loaded when you get here. We're open twenty-four hours a day, seven days a week." He smiled. "I'll knock off fifty bucks. That should almost pay for your dinner at the Presidio."

They shook hands. And then Stan asked genially, "Line up a driver yet?"

"Comedians!" Al said. "Every time I turn around —another comedian! I'll send you a check tomorrow. Have your game of golf with the senior citizens. Let's go, Mark."

When we got out to the car, Mom asked, "What happened?"

Al didn't answer. I gave Mom the hush sign and went around to unhook the trailer. Al helped me unhook it, but I knew he didn't want to go back into the garage so I hauled it in alone.

Stan was still standing where we'd left him. "What happened?" he asked. "Did I hit a nerve? Is he going to drive that car himself?"

I nodded.

"He's certainly getting thin-skinned, isn't he?"

"He's had a lot of static on the subject," I said.

"I can imagine. Well, let him learn the hard way. You going to travel with him?"

I nodded.

"Do what you can, huh? He's kind of—juvenile. Always has been. Keep an eye on him."

"I'll do my best," I promised, "but I'm only a growing boy and he's the boss."

In the car, Al and Mom were sitting in the front seat, staring through the windshield, very quiet. I said, "That's over. Now let's enjoy the sun and look forward to that fifty-dollar dinner tonight."

We had lunch in Old Town and then went across on the ferry to Coronado. There was a tennis tournament being run there on one of the hotel courts. Al and I weren't fans, but Mom had won a couple county championships as a junior and we enjoyed watching her enjoy it. It wasn't too dull a sport and Mom kept us informed as to who was winning and why and like that.

So everything was free and easy by the time we arrived at the Presidio Sky Room. Mom and Al ordered some special kind of duck but I stayed with the standard, a sixteen-ounce porterhouse with lobster on the side. We could see all the lights of the city and the harbor as we ate, a great topper to about an eighty-three percent perfect day.

Even when we went over to pick up the engine, Mom made no comment. She was quieter riding home than she had been coming down but that could have been the natural reaction to a full and happy day. None of us talked much.

When the Duesy stopped in front of the house, I said, "I can go with you and help you unload, if you want."

Al shook his head. "Tomorrow's soon enough. Did you have a good time, Elly?"

"Perfect!" Mom said, and sighed.

Enough, I thought. *Enough. Say no more. He's a big boy now.*

"Just perfect," Mom repeated. "Thanks, Al. Good night."

The car and the trailer went down the street and we walked up to the dark house. "The fool!" Mom said. "He'll *never* grow up!"

"It's his money," I said. "He earned it."

"Money?" she said. "Who's talking about money? It's his neck I'm thinking about, his life."

"It's also *his* neck," I pointed out. "He's single."

I can't spell what she said next. Something like, "Eackch!" It was her final word for the day.

She wasn't voicing a minority opinion. Pete Lopez, Joe Moreno, Tom Winter and Stan Nowak had all said roughly the same thing and I had thought along the same line. We all worried about Al because we all liked him. He was a popular guy. But nobody ever won an automobile race on his popularity.

I helped him tear down, rebuild and install the new engine without putting myself on the time clock. Pete Lopez helped, too, just for the joy of working on equipment of that caliber. We wrapped it up in four nights and when we were finished, I think Pete and I were looking ahead to the WDTA schedule almost as much as Al was.

Maybe it was the spring. April is usually an unpredictable month in California, but the warm weather had held. We weren't the only ones affected by it. Pete, Joe and I went to a drag in Ventura on the last Sunday in the month and even those quarter-mile die-hards were talking about the new league.

The true sportsman, I think, relishes a sport with rules and limitations. A half million dollars worth of corporation-financed jet equipment shrieking across the flats at Bonneville has no competitive meaning. The next vehicle could be shot from a cannon, go even faster—and prove even less.

Drag racing was limited in length and classifications, harness racing in disciplined gait, dune buggies in texture and contour of the racing surface. Bound by these conditions, the ingenuity, the skill and the courage of the competitors was really tested. A man could compete with his peers. To me, that made it a *sport* instead of an exhibition.

Joe took a second in his class at Ventura and so did I in mine. I was edged in my final run by a Chev from San Jose, a car and a man I had beaten before but who had added a horse or two with a hotter coil.

I had never been a smiling loser but it didn't seem to bother me too much that Sunday. I must have been looking ahead to the oval tracks on the Sundays to come. If I worked the pit for Al this summer, there wouldn't be any reason for me to keep the rod; it wasn't a sensible street car. So I spread the word at Ventura that it was for sale.

Late Tuesday afternoon, as I was washing up to go home for dinner, the same man who had edged me at Ventura came into the garage, bringing a friend. This friend had brought $900 and an urge to own my roadster.

I wanted more than that for it, but how many people with $900 in cash wanted a thirty-five-year-old Ford with a Dodge engine? I signed over the pink slip to him and drove Al's pickup home for dinner.

When I showed Mom the money, she said, "Now, what?"

"I know where I can get a three-year-old Fairlane, a cream puff, a real clean two-door sedan. Don't you think it's time I settled down?"

She looked at me suspiciously. "No more drags? You?"

"No more drags. Me."

She nodded. "It's in the pattern."

"What is? Settling down?"

"You're not fooling me," she said.

"I'm not trying to, Mom. But we're not on the same wavelength."

"No more drags," she said. "And I would have to ask myself *why,* wouldn't I? And the answer comes strong and clear—because he will be driving Al Duncan's double overhead clambake, that's why."

"Camshaft," I corrected her.

"Well, at least you admit it," she said.

"I admit Al's car has two overhead camshafts," I said patiently, "but neither Al nor I have ever suggested that I drive it. That's the gospel truth, Mom."

"But no more drags?"

"That's right. I'll be in Al's pit as his mechanic. I guess Pete Lopez will be, too."

She sighed. "I thought you two were too old to play with Al."

30

I smiled, saying nothing.

"Should we cook outside?" she asked. "It's such a nice evening. Would you start the charcoal?"

I had the charcoal ready by the time she had made the salad. She brought out the rolls and hamburger patties and I was the chef. She seemed unusually quiet and I didn't have much to say. I was kind of down. I guess it was because I'd sold the roadster. We'd been partners a long time.

I was turning the hamburgers when Mom said, "I suppose you think I'm a sour old fuddy-duddy?"

"Never! At least not since I was five. What's the matter? Bad day at the library?"

"Turning my fledgling loose," she said, "that's what's the matter. Watching my chickadee sprout wings."

"You're on another frequency again," I said.

"You sold your hot-rod," she said. "It's . . . another step. It's like selling a paper route."

"I didn't mind selling my paper route," I said, "and I won't miss the roadster after a couple of days."

"That's right," she said, "you did have a paper route, didn't you?"

I nodded. I moved the rolls closer to the fire to brown them.

"I guess you've *always* worked, haven't you? Some childhood you've had!"

"I'm not kicking. I have this lenient mother and

this good-natured boss and great big Bermuda on- ions for my hamburger and . . .”

“You’re a man,” she said. “You’ve had to be and you’ve been one. Ever since your father died. Would I sound sloppy if I said I admire you almost as much as I love you?”

“Hey, Ma!” I said. “Hey!” My voice choked in my throat.

“Don’t panic,” she said. “I’m not cracking up. Certain things have to be said and this is the time. You’re a man and this is a man’s world so I can’t even hope to understand it. But if Al wants you to drive that—that silly contraption of his, you have my permission.”

I smiled and handed her a hamburger. “Thanks. But I don’t think you have to worry about that. It’s the furthest thing from his mind right now.”

“Now,” she said. “But later? Al’s not stupid. He’s crazy, but he’s a long way from being stupid. He’ll learn who the driver is in your combination soon enough.”

I am not exactly a brilliant conversationalist. I came back with my previous line. “Hey, Ma! Hey!”

“Hey, yourself.”

“Where did you learn that word? That’s a racing term—the combination.”

“Don’t I know it? Didn’t your father always say it? It’s the combination that counts; he must have told me that a hundred times.”

chapter THREE

THE ADAGE IS AS OLD AS THE GAME—IT'S THE combination that counts in racing. The driver, the mechanic, the car—each of these is equally important in the winning combination.

A stubborn man with a dream could mess up the combination. There were a number of successful and experienced drivers Al could have lured to our stable with the promise of that Nowak four. But Al had to be the hero in his own dream and the only place for a hero was behind the wheel.

"And how can we be sure he won't be all right?" Pete Lopez said Wednesday night. "We've been downgrading him without knowing anything about him."

"He's been away from it too long," I said. "And I'd guess the men he'll be running against are a lot sharper than the kids he and my dad used to race against."

"That's a good guess," Pete said, "but we don't know it's true. Maybe Al's a natural."

"I hope so. We'll hold our thumbs."

I stopped holding mine Sunday afternoon. Al, Pete and I took the Nowak up to Linus for her shakedown cruise. Linus would be on the WDTA schedule and the track owner was giving us a couple of pre-season Sundays to check out our equipment.

We were the first to arrive. Two sprinkler trucks were still out on the track and the tunnel to the infield was just being unlocked as we drove up.

It was a well conditioned mile of banked dirt at Linus. Some of the greatest names in racing had learned their trade there. According to the papers, the USAC hadn't been too happy about the owner signing up with the WDTA. But as of that Sunday no official action had been taken to cancel the USAC sanction. Nor had any action been taken to prevent drivers and owners from belonging to both organizations.

It wasn't likely that the name drivers in the USAC would be racing in the new league. They had their own busy schedule and would think twice about risking their expensive equipment for the smaller purses in the WDTA.

We were unloading the Nowak from its trailer when a brand new white Caddy came out of the infield end of the tunnel and headed our way.

"Here comes the big man in the big car," Al said. "We're getting an official welcome."

It was Jack Belmont, owner of the track. He was a

34

tall, thin man, looked like a western movie star. "Lead-foot Duncan," he said, "back to the wars. Are these your sons, Al?"

"I never married," Al said. "This is Luke Devlin's son, Mark, and this is Pete Lopez. Shake hands with a millionaire, boys."

"Millionaire, huh!" Mr. Belmont said. "That'll be the day!"

"If not today, tomorrow," Al said. "Remember the Fourth of July I creamed you in the feature at San Valdesto?"

"My memory isn't that good. Where'd you get the car?"

"Most of it from Tom Winter, all except the engine."

"And the engine?"

"From Stan Nowak."

Mr. Belmont's eyebrows went up. "You mean business, don't you?"

"I figured I might need a few extra horses," Al explained. "I can't be sure the old touch is what it used to be."

Mr. Belmont laughed. "Touch? Mark's dad had the touch. All you ever had was your foot, Al."

"You admitted your memory is bad and now you've proved it. When are those water trucks going to get off the track?"

"As soon as I think they should. Take it easy, old-timer. You'll have all afternoon to practice." He winked at me. "And a whole summer to learn. Pleased to have met you boys." He nodded and went back to his car.

Pete turned his head away so Al couldn't catch his smile. I went over to the pickup truck to get the extra tires. Al stood where he was, staring at the long, high, whitewashed stands across the track. It was an old plant but well preserved. Al could have been dreaming of a past appearance here or looking forward to the next.

Pete came over to help me with the tires. "Still holding your thumbs?" he asked quietly.

"One thumb. I don't like what Mr. Belmont said about Al's foot."

"It could have been a joke. Those old-timers needle each other a lot."

"And usually with reason. Well, we're just hired help, right?"

"Wrong," Pete said. "We're two-thirds of a team. Let's never forget that. He may be a little kooky, but he's *our* Al."

By the time the water trucks had finished and left the track, about half a dozen cars had arrived and been unloaded, all front-engine jobs, not one of them a clunker.

Gus Mayer's Offy was in the next pit; a couple of his boys came over to help us push the Nowak to a start.

Al's new helmet glistened in the noon sun and

those knobby rear tires dug into the dirt under the brake of compression and then there was a "var-room" from four hungry cylinders and our hero was under way.

One of Mayer's boys asked, "Didn't you used to race jalopies at Canyon City?"

I nodded. "Mark Devlin's my name. This is Pete Lopez."

"I'm Les Pardee," he said. "My brother, Bill, used to run at Canyon City and I worked for him."

"I remember him. What's he doing now?"

"He runs a service station in Laguna Beach. He still wants me to work for him. I like it better here, don't you?"

"So far," I said. "But I'm not looking forward to the afternoon in Canyon City."

He grinned. "Maybe it won't look so bad from the pit."

The light blue Nowak was breezing through the backstretch now, raising no dust on the damp track. Her song sounded mellow to me. Al probably wouldn't be trying for any fast laps on this trip but I took out the watch just the same.

Les Pardee came over to ask if we'd help him push their car to a start.

We waited until Al had gone by before pushing the Offy into action.

That put two cars on the track in view of a grow-ing audience in the pits. Pete said, "No duels now.

No show-off stuff, please, Al! You're not ready for show-off stuff."

"You're reading my mind," I said.

Nothing of the sort developed on this first trial. Al took four easy laps without a challenge from Gus and came coasting into the pit. His fastest lap had been over fifty seconds.

"How'd she act?" I asked.

"Okay. Fine." He shook his head. "That old touch doesn't come back overnight, I guess. Want to try her?"

"If you insist," I said, playing it casual. "It just happens I brought my helmet."

"What a coincidence!" Pete said.

Gus Mayer had pulled in; there was no other car on the track when I took off for my first trip on a mile track, my first trip in a car *designed* for racing, not converted for it.

I'd driven my old Chev on the shorter track at Canyon City, but this was entirely different. This car went where you pointed it, answered every summons without hesitation, happily at home on the surface it was tailored for.

I took two exploratory laps and put a little more right foot into the third. I didn't exactly bury the fence but I was throwing dirt most of the way around the turns and the Nowak was breathing pretty hard.

When I came in, a lap later, Pete was smiling and

Al was frowning. Les Pardee called over, "You never looked that good at Canyon City."

"She handle all right?" Al asked.

I nodded.

"It's about time for lunch," he said.

We had brought our lunches. We sat on the infield grass in the shade of the truck. A couple of other drivers and "mechs" came over to shoot the breeze, including Tudi Petrini.

Tudi had grown up in Italy and had worked both as a mechanic and co-driver for some of the best in Europe. He had become an American citizen five years ago and a successful USAC campaigner. But the dirt was his true love; he was all WDTA now. He probably would have been voted most-likely-to-succeed in the new league.

I saw him in action about an hour later, an illustrated lecture on how to cover a mile of dirt in the shortest possible time. I tried to study his lines into the turns. I listened for the sounds of deceleration and acceleration, trying to plot his strategy.

And then I realized that was *his* strategy, based on the car he was driving, putting his strengths to the best use. I might have other strengths, and no two cars handle exactly alike.

And why should I study another man's driving? I was a mech.

Al had been watching, too, like a bush leaguer

watching Willie Mays. He said, "I'm going to try a few more laps. Time my third one."

We pushed him to a start and came back to the pit. Pete said, "I hope he's not out there to prove anything. Even he must know he's not Tudi Petrini —yet."

I didn't answer. Petrini had pulled in, but there were still a couple of cars out on the track, Duke Manchester in a D-O, Red Nelsen in an offset Chev.

Duke came in as Al was starting his second lap, Red was about half a lap away and not pushing it. I breathed easier.

But Red was moving slower than I'd thought. As Al came charging past the pit for the start of his third lap, the Chev was only a quarter of a lap ahead and still loafing. Al tried to go by on the far turn— and Red decided not to let him.

All the heads came up in the pits as the dark blue Chev and the light blue Nowak fought it out through the turn. Red had gone high and Al had the lower, shorter line, but the Chev came gunning off the bank to keep the lead into the straightaway.

Al gained on him there; I thought he had an easy chance to keep his edge through the south. He slowed too early. Red stole the groove and came out into the backstretch leading by twenty feet.

"That's enough now," Pete muttered. "Easy does it, boss."

Al didn't quit. The light blue blob seemed to leap.

It moved past the dark blue blob halfway through the stretch and went flying toward the turn, widening the daylight between the two cars, streaking wildly toward disaster.

Every pair of eyes in the pits was on that north turn now and every man there knew Al would never make it at that speed. There was a screech of tortured tires and the bark of deceleration as the blue car went sliding up the bank.

The Nowak couldn't have been more than a foot short of the fence when Al finally gained control, the engine still running. Dust billowed across the infield as the Chev moved past us, once again loafing. The Nowak came down the bank slowly, like a wounded tiger, and headed for the pits.

"I forgot to put the watch on him," I said.

"Don't worry. He won't be interested in the time."

When he pulled in, Al's face was grim. "Some show, huh? Outfoxed by a converted Chev!"

"It'll take a while," I said. "It'll come back. That's why we're here, to learn."

He pulled off his helmet. "Maybe Jack Belmont was right about me. Maybe I was all foot. You needed more foot with those engines. But this thing —it's like a bomb!"

"We have a whole afternoon left," I said, "and next Sunday. It'll take time."

"Sure," he said. "Sure. They must have been laughing in the pits, huh?"

"I don't think anybody was laughing," I said. "You came awful close to going through that fence."

He nodded. He stepped out of the car and stretched. I thought he looked a little pale. He went over to the water jug. Pete looked at me and I looked at Pete, neither of us knowing what to say. An Al Duncan without confidence was a strange new sight to us.

He practiced some more that afternoon and so did I. As he explained it: "I won't be able to drive in all the races on some of those mixed cards this summer. Besides, it's always good to have an understudy."

By the time we were loading up to go home, some of his confidence seemed to be back. Several of the drivers had dropped over to needle him and he had grinned through it, answering in kind.

Pete's mother worked on Sundays so he was having dinner at my house. Al dropped us off there after we'd unloaded the car at the garage.

Mom was in the kitchen, making enchiladas. "Well," she said, "the boy mechanics! And how did Daredevil Duncan do this afternoon?"

Pete laughed. I said, "He lived up to our expectations."

Mom sighed. "That bad, eh? Is there hope for the future?"

I shrugged. Mom looked at Pete. He shrugged.

"You're not very talkative," she said. "What happened?"

"Nothing serious," I said. "It's been a hot, noisy, dusty day."

"There'll be more of them," she said. "A whole summer full of them. There's a pitcher of iced tea in the refrigerator."

We took the iced tea out to the table under the fig tree and later we ate the enchiladas out there. Coolness came when the sun went down, and my mood changed with the temperature.

As Mom had said, there were a lot of Sundays to come. Al had to get better. He might not improve enough to be a winner in what seemed to be shaping up as a rough league, but his wrench and the genius of Stan Nowak gave us two-thirds of the combination we needed. The final third, the driver, was really all we had to worry about.

chapter FOUR

THE NEXT SUNDAY WAS COOLER BUT NOT much more comforting. Al had tried too hard last week; this week he didn't try hard enough. Maybe he was worried about laughter in the pits, maybe he was starting to believe his critics. Whatever the reason, he turned in a lot of tame laps.

He had his own explanation: "It's not the same, *alone* out there. It's different in competition. Don't look so sour; I'm going to be all right, once the action starts."

Because of Al's lack of interest, yours truly, boy mechanic, clocked a lot of mileage that afternoon. I didn't need the competition to make it fun for me; the car and the track were enough. A man could always compete with himself, against the timer and against his own potential. And I could certainly use the practice.

There were more cars at the track, but not all of them were up to last week's level. There were a few home garage jobs with converted engines, rodders moving up. But the scene was the same, color and noise and dust and an excitement in the air.

Les Pardee called it. "It's kind of like a rehearsal for a show, isn't it? I mean—nobody knows how the show is going to turn out or how the actors are going to do but everybody's looking ahead to the opening."

The opening would be at Fulton next week, a mixed card. There would be two ten-milers, two twenty-five-milers and a fifty-mile feature wind-up, open to the top finishers in the other races. That was in the old dirt tradition, before the 100- and 200-mile marathons became standard. We were looking ahead to it—but how about the public?

Fulton was in Nevada, which meant we would have to take off Saturday afternoon if we wanted to get there in time without driving all night. Al arranged for Joe Moreno and Red Halloran to handle the garage.

He and Mom went to a movie Friday night while Pete and I cleaned up the few jobs still unfinished at the garage.

"That Al must have saved his money," Pete commented. "He pays us overtime to do his work while he lives it up in front of the silver screen."

"A single man can save a lot of money," I said. "How much can one mouth eat?"

Pete nodded agreement. "No dependents, no responsibilities. No wonder he thinks he's still in high school."

There would be other men as old as Al racing this summer, married men and single men, with and without responsibilities. Were they, too, still emotionally in high school? The ones I had met had seemed sensible. It was certain Stan Nowak hadn't needed to campaign on the dirt. He claimed the publicity had brought him a lot of garage customers but I had never heard him claim that was the reason he raced.

It was possible the paying public wouldn't share this interest in the dirt track tradition. That wouldn't make these purists adolescents. It would make them bad guessers, a weakness not limited to children.

Fulton was in the desert and the desert was hot this time of the year. But there were people already in the stands when we came over from the motel early Sunday morning. These were the true fans, the same breed who watched the sun come up with their heroes on the practice ranges at the golf tournaments.

"It's always been a good racing town," Al told us. "Draws from all over this end of the state."

It had to be a great racing town. Though the stands were completely covered, protected from the sun, the temperature was up to ninety-seven degrees

46

and it was still morning. It would be a bad day for carburetion, dry and hot.

Al said, "We'll have to watch our tire pressure. It can really build after a couple fast laps."

So can the ridge, I thought, the loose dirt near that upper fence. That would be murder by the time the windup was ready to roll.

"Why the long face?" Al asked.

I shrugged. "The heat, I guess. I was spoiled by the air conditioning at the motel."

"You're worried about me," he said.

I shook my head.

He laughed. "You don't practice enough to be a good liar. Stop fretting, boy, and go try out the track. You'll drive the opener."

That last sentence made it about five degrees cooler. Two laps later I didn't even know the sun was out. The Nowak hadn't been told that dry air is bad for carburetion; she went singing through the stretches and around the bends without a cough, sweet and saucy.

When I came in, Pete said, "You look better every time out. Maybe, in a short race, you won't even get lapped."

"Thank you for your expression of confidence. I'll say this much—if I get lapped it won't be the car's fault. She's ready!"

That was one of the advantages I had in my

WDTA debut, the readiness of the car. The other was the quality of the field. There were ten entries. Four of them were conversions and neither Gus Mayer nor Tudi Petrini was driving any of the other six.

I started on the rail in the second row. That's a strategic spot for a good driver; the leaders are in sight and he's out of the heavy traffic of the early laps. It could make a not-so-good driver nervous; all the eager beavers from behind would be breathing down his neck. I was nervous.

The line-up had been decided by lot. Red Nelsen's Chev was on the pole. A local boy in an ancient Cragar flanked him. Chris Tyler in his yellow D-O flanked me. Based on past performances, Chris would be the man to beat in this one. He grinned over at me confidently and I grinned back to keep it even.

All the engines were running now and the starter signaled us forward for the flying lap. I didn't glance toward the pit; I didn't want to see Al looking as nervous as I felt. I kept my attention on the car that would set the pace, Nelsen's Chev.

He set an easy pace and the lines must have stayed even. Because the green flag dropped as we came gunning past the pits for the first time.

Both Red and the local boy floored at the same time; they took off together. But the Chev had the steam and Red had the groove. The Cragar sailed high on the bank as the boy tried to manhandle it back toward the lower track.

It took him a second too long. The Nowak went skinning through the gap before he could close it and Chris trailed right behind me. The Cragar had gone from second to fourth in 200 feet.

Red was setting a pace I didn't try to match. The gap grew through the first lap. Chris went past me in the backstretch of the second lap. I was now in third place, about fifty feet in front of the Cragar. One clunker had already limped into the pits.

Chris continued to move up on Red. I tried to put some daylight between me and the kid in the Cragar.

He didn't turn out to be my problem. Duke Manchester came shooting past him in the fourth lap, crowding my deck as we made the swing into the grandstand lane.

Duke had more experience. I had more car. We paced it out through the stretch and I held enough of an advantage into the next turn to stay in front all through it.

I was moving faster than I had planned to but the Nowak's steadiness bolstered my confidence. We fought it out—and I held my edge.

It was ding-dong through three torrid laps and then Duke began to fall back. And as the Nowak and I swept around the grandstand turn into the eighth lap, I saw Red Nelsen's Chev heading into the pits. We were in second place!

49

Chris was leading the pack and he was almost a quarter lap away. I didn't try to catch him; it would have taken more than I cared to risk at the time. I kept an eye open for any challengers coming up from behind and I finished second, still almost a quarter of a lap behind Chris Tyler.

Both Pete and Al congratulated me when I came in, but Al didn't look quite as happy as Pete. With all that clear and unchallenged ground between me and the winner, Al must have wondered why I hadn't made my move.

So I said, "I didn't figure I could catch Chris in two laps."

Al nodded. "That's a lot of car he's driving."

Pete grinned. "You might have caught the car—if Chris hadn't been driving it."

"You could be right," I admitted. "For the first time in history, you could be right. But I'll learn. There are better drivers in this league than Chris Tyler."

Pete sighed. "Ain't that the truth!"

I laughed. But Al didn't. He had been unusually quiet since I'd pulled in. I hoped he wasn't thinking that I had finished second and he had to do as well. I wasn't here to compete with my boss. And he would be in a faster field.

Mike Kaprelian won the second ten-miler in a field even slower than mine had been. Petrini, Mayer and some of the other real aces would open in the twenty-five-mile run that Al had picked for his debut.

His quiet mood lasted as we checked out the car. He had watched these boys from the stands and the pits in the years since he had last been a competitor. He had run against them in his imagination. But in the past few weeks he had been out where the action was and he had to know now that this was a different game from the county fair circuit he and my dad had traveled. *These* were the professionals.

The stands were almost full, despite the heat. All the drivers and mechs not working on their cars stood in whatever shade they could find, talking quietly. The lemonade and soft drink hawkers were getting rich.

There would be twelve cars in six rows. Our baby blue bomb would start on the rail in the fourth row, smack in the middle of the heavy traffic. Al was going to be short on elbow room in the early laps.

Both Tudi Petrini and Gus Mayer were back in the ruck, though nobody expected them to stay there for long. Chris Tyler was on the pole, flanked by Harry Shaw.

The engines were turning now; the starter signaled them into their paced lap. Pete said, "Hold your thumbs again. Al's got me scared."

"Why?"

"He's so quiet. He's not naturally a quiet man."

"It's hot," I said. "He's had a long trip. And he's opening in fast company."

"That last reason, that's the one," Pete said. "That's why I'm scared. I just hope Al isn't out there to prove he's faster than the company."

"That's why they're all out there," I said.

"I know, I know! But remember what he told us last Sunday, that he was going to be all right, once the action started? It's the competition that brings out the tiger in Al. He should have driven that opener. That would have been more his speed."

"Relax," I said. "He's no fool. He knows what he's up against."

The field was moving through the backstretch, throwing dust into the motionless air. Tyler and Shaw were leading an orderly parade toward the green flag. As they came around the north turn, the sound grew suddenly louder, echoing off the stands across the way. It was going to be a fast start.

The south turn snarl had me holding my breath. The first three rows had jumped as one car when the flag dropped. For about five seconds it looked as if none of them would get through the turn. Decks bumped, hubs rubbed and tires squealed. Then Shaw came shooting out of the knot with Tyler trailing and there was steering room.

In the tornado of dust I could see a flash of light blue hugging the lower track where the going was

52

still clear. Two cars went past it before the back-stretch was spanned. Our entry now rode ninth in a field of twelve.

"The worst is over," Pete said. "There can't be another traffic jam like that one!"

I nodded, watching the blue car skim around the north turn. If competition was his spur, Al wasn't responding to it in this first lap. The three men behind were no faster; he came past the pits still ninth.

Petrini had charged out of the ruck in that first turn tangle; he was now chasing Tyler and Shaw as they seesawed for the lead. Gus Mayer had not made as quick a move; he rode unchallenged in seventh place, biding his time. The field was beginning to string out after that wild start.

Only the three in front kept up the pace of the first lap. Tyler and Shaw were still trading the lead on every turn as Petrini crept up on them from behind.

The crowd was rooting for Petrini. Crowds love super-stars, particularly if the super-star is only five feet, four inches tall and full of vinegar.

Tudi had one advantage. Both Shaw and Tyler could use only that section of the track not occupied by the other. Tudi had the choice of his own line into the turns and all the track he needed for his con-trolled slides. He stayed within striking distance, waiting for the duel ahead to be decided.

Gus Mayer was moving up, dogging Mike Kaprelian out of the south turn, edging past him in the backstretch. Al still rode ninth, with no challenge from behind, with no change in the gap between him and the car riding eighth.

Petrini made his move in the eleventh lap. Tyler had temporarily dropped behind Shaw. Tudi took him, in front of all his fans, in grandstand lane. Ahead, Shaw put a little more right foot into his mount but Petrini lost no ground.

"What's the matter with our boy?" Pete asked. "I didn't think being too careful was going to be his problem."

"He's still in the same lap as the leaders," I said, "and the race is almost half over."

He was riding eighth a lap later as the local driver holding down that spot came steaming into the pits. A quarter of a lap behind him, Shaw and Petrini were starting to close in on the tail-enders. We chalked an "8" and a "12" on the blackboard to inform Al he was riding eighth through the twelfth lap.

He'd signaled that he'd seen it as Petrini and Shaw broadsided into the front straightaway. They had already lapped the last place car.

Maybe Al heard the roar of Petrini's fans. Or maybe he had planned to make his move in the twelfth lap. He began to eat up the yardage between him and Mike Kaprelian.

Mike had let Gus Mayer go by without a fight, but he didn't extend the same courtesy to Al. He increased his pace just as the Nowak's nose drew even with his rear wheels.

Now we'd know which Al was out there, the tiger of that first Sunday's practice session or the pussy cat of the second. Mike had the best line and the best traction; the track was already loose and treacherous above the middle of the bank. Our sure-footed lady rode it without skittering, hanging close to Mike's mount, losing no ground through the long turn.

"Hey!" Pete said.

"Hey, hey," I agreed. "Al's looking pretty solid, isn't he?"

Pete nodded. "But I was thinking of the car. She's really finding traction in that rough going."

"You can thank Al for that, too," I said. "The engine is Nowak's, but that suspension system is all Al's."

They both finally beat Mike Kaprelian, Nowak's horses on the stretches, Al's handiwork on the bends. We rode into the sixteenth lap in seventh place, less than five lengths behind Chris Tyler.

Tudi Petrini had taken over first place by this time and he was all alone and winging, a quarter of a lap in front of Shaw and Mayer as they battled it out for second.

Pete said, "You know something? Al's traveled those last four laps faster than Petrini!"

It didn't seem logical but it had to be true. In the twelfth lap Tudi had been three-quarters of a lap in front; he now had less than a half lap lead on our lady.

"So it can't be just the car," Pete said. "You were right the first time—Al's looking mighty solid." He smiled. "I guess he's going to be our star, huh?"

I played it straight, not reacting to his needle. "Who else?" I asked.

Al was gaining on Chris Tyler now. The song of Tyler's engine sounded a little sour to me but maybe it was something I wanted to hear. Al moved past him in the eighteenth lap.

"That's the guy who beat you in the opener," Pete said.

"You keep telling me things I know. I think Chris is having fuel problems."

Pete chuckled.

A lap later Tyler's car came slowly into the pits, spitting and coughing.

"You have a good ear," Pete said.

Gus Mayer had finally worked his way past Shaw. He was closing in on Petrini. Al still rode sixth.

I said, "Sixth place won't earn us a chance in the finale."

"You've already qualified with your second place," Pete said. "It's the car that qualifies, not the driver."

"I know it," I said. "I just wanted to hear you admit it."

Al finished better than sixth. Dutch Krueger blew a tire on the twenty-fourth lap and Al finished fifth. We had the water jug and a cold, wet towel waiting for him in the pit.

The sun and the dust had burned his face between the bandanna and his goggles. He buried his face in the towel.

When he came up for air, Pete told him, "You were great. It's too bad Mr. Belmont wasn't here to see it."

Al managed a smile. "He'll see me soon enough. You guys had me pegged for a wild man, didn't you?"

"Not lately," I said. "Not after last Sunday. You were right—you need the competition."

He sat there, breathing heavily. "Petrini win?"

I nodded. "Gus Mayer was second. Don't you think you should get over in the shade?"

"As soon as I can move I'll get out. Man, I couldn't have driven two more laps!"

There were fifty miles still in front of him, fifty miles on a track rougher than this had been. I said, "A little rest and you'll be ready again."

He shook his head. "I'll never make that windup. I'm not in condition for the long ones, not yet. Do you want to try it?"

I wish I could relate how I led that blue-ribbon field through every one of fifty screaming laps, setting a new track record every lap.

But this isn't a movie. Halfway through the second lap the mag shorted and burned itself out. We didn't even stay around to see who won.

chapter FIVE

LARRY BEAM, RENOWNED CLASS PRESIDENT,
gave the commencement address. He titled it "America, This Way Up!" and I thought it was pretty good.
It was mostly about how a young man could achieve
success in this country if he chose a trade he liked,
worked hard and used his noodle.

Pete didn't think much of the speech. "Phony,"
Pete said. "He'll spend the summer in Europe as his
graduation present. Then he'll put in four years at
Princeton and come home to run his papa's bank.
That's how *he'll* work his way up!"

"He wasn't talking to himself," I explained. "The
speech was for us, and I think it was kind of him to
explain the obvious to us poor working slobs."

Pete sniffed.

"To tell you the truth," I went on, "I feel sorry for
Larry Beam."

"I can't wait to hear why."

"He'll never have a chance to prove himself. Even

59

if he hits the jackpot, he'll never be sure he could have done it from scratch."

Pete sighed. "How terrible that would be! To be rich and not know why? I don't see how a man could stand it!"

"Okay, cynic, I'll ask you a question. Where would you rather be this summer—in Europe or out on that WDTA circuit?"

"What's that got to do with the speech Beam made? Racing, is that a way up?"

"It sure is. It's my way."

"Up to what?"

"Who knows? I figure if a guy gets good enough at what he likes to do there'll be room for him somewhere upstairs."

Pete shook his head. "I thought it was Al's idea. When did you decide racing was going to be your trade?"

"About halfway through Larry's speech," I said.

Pete laughed.

He thought I was joking, but Larry's speech had started me to thinking about where I was heading. And it was clear enough to me that I was heading toward where I had always lived—the world of the automobile.

There were a number of roads in that world. One of them could lead to your name on the big cup at Indianapolis and another to the presidency of General Motors. There were shorter, lower roads. Al and

Tom Winter had followed one of them. So had Jack Belmont. So had Les Pardee's brother, who ran a filling station in Laguna Beach.

I was in the right world; it really didn't matter if I was a driver or mechanic. At least that's what I tried to tell myself.

The mag that had burned out had come from one of the best men in the business, Tony Turner, so there was no point in replacing it with a different make. We went back to Tony and got his newer, better model, a 50,000-volt jolter.

We would be making the first of our two trips to Linus this Sunday. The second stop would be the last race of the season, a 100-mile run that could decide the season's champion. This Sunday's card followed the pattern of Fulton: two tens, two twenty-fives and a fifty.

Stan Nowak had come up to watch the action. He and Jack Belmont were in Petrini's pit when we unloaded. They both came over to chin with Al, bringing their needles.

"I heard about your lucky fifth at Fulton," Belmont said.

"It must have been the engine," Stan added.

"It was the engine that kept me back in fifth place," Al admitted. "We did all right, considering the condition of that magneto you probably picked up in a junkyard."

"That was a Turner mag," Stan protested.

"Even a Turner mag doesn't last forever," Al said. "Ask one of your mechanics."

Belmont laughed. Pete and I looked the other way. Stan looked straight at Al, his face flushed.

Al smiled. "You want to keep dishing it out—or should we talk like friends, which we are?"

They talked as friends, using shorter needles. One was a promoter, one a designer and one a driver-mechanic. But they had all come from the same background, competing on the dirt; they were brothers.

Les Pardee came over from Gus Mayer's pit to tell me, "You won't have it so easy in the opener today. Gus is going to let me drive."

"I'm scared already," I said. "I didn't have it too easy last week. I took second."

"Sure, but Chris Tyler was in it. He's passing up the opener today. All the hotshots are. That's why Gus is letting me drive."

"Good luck," I said. "I hope you finish a clean second."

"I'm going to try for better than that, with Nowak watching," he said quietly, too quiet for Stan to hear.

"What's he—your personal critic?"

"He's a man looking for a driver. Why do you think he's here?"

"You tell me."

"Roy Gaskin is retiring. Stan's here to find a new man."

Gaskin had driven all of Nowak's Indy entries— and finished in the money almost every year.

I said, "There must be a lot of USAC drivers who aren't signed up for next year."

"I don't know about that. All I know is he's here and he's been asking Gus for a rundown on the young drivers."

"Why young? What's wrong with experience?"

"Go over and ask him."

"I'm not pushy enough," I said.

"Well, get pushy for a few seconds. I need one. You, too, Pete."

Pete and I went over to help push the Offy to a start. When we came back, Al was alone in the pit.

"Stan is looking for a driver," he said. "A *young* driver."

"Why young?"

"So he can work with him through the years. He wants a man young enough to have a future—with Stan."

"You sound bitter," Pete said.

Al shook his head. "Not me. The dirt, that's my home. And who wants to drive for a man who uses junk magnetos? Let's get the lady ready to roll."

It was an overcast morning, damp and cool. The Nowak started after only a few yards of pushing; that new mag really threw a flame.

"You know," Pete said, "I don't think he is bitter. He really loves the dirt, doesn't he?"

I nodded. "He never planned to make money this summer. This is his vacation."

"An amateur," Pete said. "I mean—in the right way, a guy who loves the sport."

Maybe, I thought, that was why Stan Nowak was looking for a young driver. Many of the older men here had raced in the USAC, a few under the old Triple-A banner. There was more money in the USAC and a longer racing season. But most of the older drivers here had other businesses they weren't likely to desert; this was a sport to them. To the young ones this was just another step on the long road to the big money.

Les Pardee went by, giving us the haughty nod. Al loafed through the backstretch. Mike Kaprelian edged out onto the track. The infield refreshment stand was opening.

"I'm hungry," Pete said.

"Wait until Al finishes his run. Maybe he'll pop for a hamburger. Do you have a watch?"

He handed it to me but I never used it. Al loafed through five laps and came in. "I'm hungry," he said.

"So are we," I said. "We figured as long as you're not paying us you'd pop for some hamburgers."

He frowned. "I'm paying you. It was a percentage deal, remember? One-third of all purses, minus expenses."

"I don't want it," I said. "I've decided I'm here for the sun and the fun."

"Me, too," Pete said. "The sun and the fun and the hamburgers."

"Kids!" Al said. "All kids are crazy these days!"

"All three of us," I admitted.

He looked at me suspiciously. "You figure this is the road to Indianapolis, do you?"

"It could be," I said. "How about the hamburgers? Or do we have to break open our piggy banks?"

"Kids!" he said again. "Kids! Let's go. I'll buy."

We were easy on him. Pete had three, I had two. And then I went out into the overcast to put the lady through her paces. She was a perfect lady through all of them, skimming the turns, charging the stretches, breezing or blasting, not a cough, not a hiccup. I finished with a hot lap and a cool one and came in to see that Al had the watch in his hand.

"You were *moving!*" he said.

"It must be the new mag."

"It was you. You'll drive the opener." He paused. "And the windup, too. Maybe you can show Nowak something."

I shook my head. "You didn't come here to be a mechanic. You can be a mechanic at home."

"Don't go noble on me," he said. "Anything I can't stand, it's a young martyr."

I could feel the blood coming up into my face.

65

Pete chuckled. Al looked at me evenly. "Don't you want to drive the windup?"

"No," I lied.

"So, okay, you won't. Why are we getting so grim?"

I smiled. "I don't know, Al. Maybe we won't even qualify for the windup."

"We'll qualify," he promised me. "One of us will qualify. I guarantee it."

This would be my third start in the Nowak; there was no reason for me to be as tense as I was. I would be only one of many its designer would be watching. The friction with Al had been trivial and nothing new. We always spoke our minds.

Reason or not, the tension was there, an ache between my shoulder blades, an uneasiness in my stomach. It didn't help to learn I would start on the pole.

"What's fretting you?" Pete asked.

"I don't know. I'm nervous."

"Don't try to prove anything, buddy. The fun and the sun and the hamburgers—that's why we're here, remember?"

"That's only part of it," I said. "If there weren't any other cars here, we wouldn't be here, either."

He grinned. "Speak for yourself. I'm any place where a man will buy me a hamburger. With seven kids in the family, Ma's grocery budget doesn't include much meat. Smile, amigo; you're where you want to be."

That I was. And what did it matter who was watching or why? The weather was perfect, the car was ready, there was a race to be run, win or lose.

It was a young field, including a couple of local boys in their own creations, both Chev-powered. The only engine in it that ranked with the Nowak was Gus Mayer's Offy, which would be driven by Les Pardee.

I knew Les had driven his brother's car a few times at Canyon City but I didn't know what other racing experience he'd had. He would start on the outside in the third row. One of the local Chevs flanked me.

I will relate the rest as quickly and modestly as possible. The Chev that flanked me led in the race for 200 feet, beating me at the jump-off. But for the other nine miles and 5,080 feet the Nowak was too much for all of them. I had my first WDTA win. Les Pardee finished fourth.

"You looked like a champ all the way," Pete told me.

"Stan Nowak, please notice," Al said. "You were great, Mark."

"Thank the car and the weather," I said, "and the rookie field. I needed all of 'em."

Al shook his head. "You'd have been great in any company. You're your father's son, all right."

I still knew I had won in a rookie field, of course, but a win is a win and food for the ego. I developed a false sense of my own ability. It didn't last out the day.

The sun had burned off the overcast and the temperature had gone up by the time Al was ready to try his luck in the twenty-five-mile run. The temperature would still be lower than it had been at Fulton, but the company he would compete against would be roughly the same.

It didn't seem to bother him. He looked and sounded cheerful and confident, joking with Chris Tyler's gang in the next pit. This new, cool Al had been born on the second Sunday of practice and I wondered how temporary the change would be.

I remembered what Mom had said: Al might be crazy but he was a long way from being stupid. According to Belmont, Al had been a lead-foot as a kid. But he had seen a lot of races and a lot of changes since those wild days—and he was not stupid. Maybe the new Al was the real one.

It lasted through the afternoon. He drove an even better race than he had last Sunday against most of the same gang. He didn't finish as high; he finished sixth. He had been luckier last week because some of the cars in front of him had conked out in the desert heat.

He came in looking tired but resigned.

I said, "You drove better and had less luck."

He nodded. "I think that's right. But how much better do I have to get?"

"Two percent," I said. "The winner finished half a mile ahead in twenty-five miles. That's two percent."

He smiled. He climbed out and stretched. He asked, "Do you want to stay to watch the windup?"

I looked at him suspiciously.

"Think what you want," he said. "I'm too tired to drive it. I'm not going to risk my neck and the necks of the rest of the gang just to prove I'm an iron man—which I'm not."

"Okay," I said. "I'll drive it."

Later, when Al was over in Mayer's pit, Pete said, "Was he telling the truth. Or does he want you to show Nowak your stuff?"

"Both, maybe," I said. "I don't know. He's changed, hasn't he?"

"Maybe we read him wrong," Pete said. "Maybe he just wants to be here and be part of it, on the track or in the pit. Working on other people's cars can get boring. This is more fun than golf or tennis or bowling."

"To Al," I qualified.

"And to us," he said. "Who are we kidding? The only difference between Al and us is birthdays."

I was still walking around in the haze of my opening win. Even the bright stars in that last race couldn't break through the fog to awe me.

I started up front, on the rail in the second row.

All of the brighter stars were behind me, Petrini and Shaw and Mayer. Jack Belmont had an idea it would make for more action if the favorites were started in the ruck so they would have to fight their way up through the traffic.

"It's a crazy idea," Al grumbled. "Belmont's a nut!"

"He's a showman," I said. "He wants to keep the crowd happy."

Al took a deep breath. "I suppose. And I suppose that's why he's rich. Take care out there, boy. If you get tired, you just pull in. We're not here to get rich—like Jack Belmont."

I nodded.

He was looking thoughtful, as though framing words in his mind. Finally, he said, "Forget about Nowak watching, huh? He'll be watching other races this summer. This is the fastest company you've ever been in and I don't want you doing anything foolish."

"Okay, Al," I said. "I'll be careful."

All the engines were turning now; the starter was about ready to wave us into the flying lap. Al squeezed my shoulder and went back to the pit.

I didn't give you the details of my sensational win in the opener because of modesty. I don't want to give you too many details of my less-than-sensational performance in the windup, though not because of modesty.

I started with high hopes and a ready right foot and kept my ego healthy through the first lap, starting in third place, working my way up to second, behind Mike Kaprelian. I realize now why that was; the aces were still behind us and I was competing with my peers.

Mike began to pull away in the second lap and Dutch Krueger came up to challenge me in the north turn. There were too many laps still ahead; I didn't answer his challenge. I fell back to third.

I don't remember now which lap it was that Chris Tyler went by—or Red Nelsen, Shaw, Mayer, Sloan, Petrini. I remember passing Red, as he coasted into the pits. I remember I gave Tyler a strong three-lap battle before he finally took me in the grandstand stretch, where all could see.

I remember the slate informing me that in the thirty-seventh lap I was riding twelfth. Eighteen cars had started. That could mean that I was still in front of six of them or perhaps those six had dropped out. I knew Red had but maybe he was back in the running.

The haze was all gone now; the bright light of reality had taken over. Except for the duel with Tyler, I hadn't been extending the Nowak, hoping to pace myself through fifty miles on a rough track, saving something for the stretch run.

I had never driven more than five miles at Canyon City nor more than ten on a mile track. This was a whole new world, requiring techniques and stamina I didn't have at the time. My wrists ached, my right knee throbbed in pain, my mouth was parched.

I finished every one of the fifty miles but I don't know *where* to this day. Al and Pete never told me and I was never interested enough to ask.

chapter SIX

THERE IS ONE CONSOLATION IN LOSING A drag race—only the winner beats you; the loser finishes second. That is not as rough on a man's confidence as being passed by a parade. As I've mentioned, I had never been a good loser. I didn't contribute to the dialogue on the trip home.

It was one of Mom's working Sundays so she wasn't there when Al dropped me off. I spent a long time in the shower. I got rid of the dirt but the tension was still with me when I finished.

I was drinking a glass of milk in the kitchen when Mom came in. "Bad day?" she guessed.

"Fifty-fifty. I won the first race."

"Why the long face, then?"

"I drove the feature race, too, the last one. The *good* drivers were in that one."

"And you didn't do so well?"

I said nothing.

"Did you expect to? Those men are all professionals, aren't they?"

"Most of them in the last race were. But you see—there was this man—Stan Nowak. You remember, that man in San Diego?"

She nodded.

"Well, he's looking for a driver, a young driver, and he came up to Linus to check us out and . . ." I shrugged.

Mom stared at me blankly. "Driver? *Racing* driver? Aren't you one now?" She paused. "Did you have a fight with Al?"

"Of course not! But Nowak—well, that's a whole different operation. I mean, he has cars at Indianapolis and like that. I mean, that's the major league!"

"I see. What does Al think of this?"

"He's all for it."

"Hmmm!" she said.

"Hmmm, what?"

"Hmmm, Al," she answered. "That's quite a switch from his attitude of Friday night."

He and Mom had gone to a movie again on Friday night. I said nothing.

"Then it was your future he was talking about," Mom explained, "your future at the garage. Al doesn't even have any nephews, you know. You're all he has and he talked about you taking over the garage, eventually."

I stared at her.

"Of course," she went on, "that's only half of it."

"Of course," I said. "He wants to marry you, doesn't he?"

She nodded, looking at me doubtfully. There was a silence.

"Well?" she asked.

"Well, what?"

"What do you think about it?"

"It's a nice garage," I said.

Her face clouded and I figured a storm was coming. I said quickly, "I was trying to be funny. Mom, what can I say? I like Al. Al likes you. But you have to decide; it's none of my business."

She took a deep breath. "I told him I lost one husband. I told him I didn't think I wanted another I might lose any summer Sunday."

"You shouldn't have said that. That wasn't fair."

"Fair?"

"Al's what he is. He's not something you can convert to your specifications. If you like him, you like him as he is."

"Men," she said. "Men, men, men—you're all alike!"

"Not men," I said. "The half-men, the converted ones, they're all alike, like cheap, two-door sedans from an assembly line."

"And who are the half-men?"

"The men who play it safe," I said. "The men who think there's nothing in the world as important as money."

"For a boy who has earned his own keep since he was twelve years old, this scorn for money must be new."

"I don't scorn it," I said. "I just think there are more important things in the world. But who am I to tell that to a librarian?"

The storm clouds were gathering again.

"If you make the salad," I said, "I'll cook the hamburgers. Should I start the charcoal?"

There was a pause, and then she smiled. "All right. How did Al do today? Did he drive?"

"He took a sixth. But I think he drove better today than he did last Sunday. He, uh, might be getting a little too careful."

"That's a drawback, is it, being too careful?"

"I'll get the charcoal started," I said.

How can you explain to a woman about being too careful? It's the way they like to live. It's a *thing* with them, security is; they never seem to feel the need to test themselves. And they can take over a man and get him to thinking the same way. But I had talked that out with Mom before and not made my point.

The way I saw it, a man driving too fast on the freeway was a criminal, because he was risking *other people's* lives. But on a track, all the drivers had agreed to travel too fast; they had taken the calculated risk when they signed their entry forms. In that one way they were all alike. It was the only way I had noticed.

I was still not quite a human being when I went back to work Monday morning.

"Man," Al said, "you were sure sour on the ride home!"

"I'm a bad loser," I said. "Any cars to pick up?"

"Don't change the subject. You expect too much of yourself, Mark."

"I know. All bad losers expect too much of themselves. Who was it said that quitters make good losers?"

"A guy who died before you were born, a Notre Dame football coach. He was a bright guy, but not Socrates. Even Andretti loses now and then."

"Sure. But he doesn't get swamped, he doesn't get humiliated."

"Not lately," Al admitted. "But maybe he did his first year, huh?"

"Maybe. Any cars to pick up?"

He looked at me and I looked at him. Then he laughed—and I had to, also. "Aw, kid," he said, "think of that field! And this is your first year on a mile track, your first *month* on a mile track. I think you've done very, very well."

"Okay," I said. "Okay. Thanks, Al."

"You're welcome," he said. "There's a car to pick up, Doc Madison's Buick."

I took the three-wheeled cycle out to pick up Doctor Madison's Buick and my work week was officially under way. The memory of Sunday grew dim as the week went on. I liked to work on cars, all cars, stock or special. I liked to fix what was wrong and improve what was poor, to add horses or increase mileage or do anything that would make it a better car than it was when I started.

I guess it's called work therapy; by Thursday I was actually looking ahead to Sunday. And the joke in that was that I was looking ahead to a Sunday I had dreaded earlier, the race at Canyon City.

But the way I figured it now, I knew that track better than most of the other drivers knew it; nobody was likely to make a fool of me there. It was the only track on the circuit shorter than a mile. It was an odd length for an American track—a kilometer—roughly five-eighths of a mile.

"Back to the madhouse," Pete said Friday morning.

"Maybe not," I said. "Different cars, different drivers."

"And the same madhouse," Pete said.

There was a fact I'd overlooked, a fact that Les Pardee mentioned to me Sunday morning. Most of the veterans here knew this track; in its long history it had been host to every kind of wheeled racing that had been currently popular.

"So cool your dreams," he said. "The competition will be as rough as ever."

"How do you know I had dreams?"

Les grinned. "You're as young as I am and almost as dumb and I had 'em too until I remembered how long this track had been in operation."

"Is Gus going to let you drive?"

"If the car's in the race, I'll be in it. Gus doesn't want any part of this bull ring."

"Then why is he here?"

"Letting me drive is part of my pay. Otherwise, I'd be working for my brother at the station." He gestured toward the freshly painted stands across the way. "New owner?"

I shrugged.

"Same owner," Pete said. "He spruced the place up before he applied for a WDTA sanction. At least he won't be able to run those five-lap traffic jams and call them sprints."

Les laughed. "Don't make your buddy unhappy. That was his specialty, the five-lap sprints."

True enough. . . . And maybe that was why I had been successful in the ten-lap openers the last two Sundays. Pacing myself and relating to the speed of the leaders in the longer runs were things I had never had to learn until now.

We had lowered the gearing; this track was practically all turns. It was steeply banked but the surface was soft. Toward the end of a racing day, that surface became as treacherous as running on marbles.

Al came over from the truck to say, "I think maybe we'd better go to the knobby tires right away, don't you?"

"Maybe."

"Why don't you try it, first, the way she is?" he suggested. "As I remember this track, it stays hard for about twenty laps."

"As I remember it," I said, "it's usually torn up by the time the practice and qualifying sessions end."

He nodded. "Okay. We'll change the tires now. Let's go."

That had been a quick change of mind for a man who usually prepared for a race as carefully as Al did. I said, "I could be wrong."

"I know," he said. "So can I. I never had any luck on this track. Your father rode it as if he owned it but it was always poison for me." He paused. "So I'll go with your hunch. As I said before, you're your father's son."

I had a strange sense of being in a time warp when I drove out to test the oversize knobbies half an hour later. In my dad's youth there had probably been a lot of half-mile tracks and this one had been even longer, five-eighths of a mile. Only midgets and jalopies used tracks this size today; only tradition was keeping it on the WDTA schedule.

There was some clay in the track and it was still firm when I took the blue lady out to try her footing. That made the ride bumpy. I knew it would change as the track softened under the churning rear wheels of the cars still in the pits but it didn't prove anything now. I drove two tame laps and came in.

"Too early to know?" Al asked.

I nodded.

"What do you think?"

"As she is, I *think*. But you're the boss."

"Not here," he said. "You'll do it all today." He grinned and added, "Don't panic; Nowak won't be watching."

The memory of last week came back but I didn't rise to the bait. It was only a temper test; he wanted to be sure I wasn't going into today's action with the wrong attitude.

There would be three thirty-lap races acting as qualifiers for the finale of the day, a fifty-lap run. And Al wanted me to do all the driving.

"It's not my kind of track," he explained. "Okay with you?"

I nodded. "Maybe I won't even qualify for the last race. But if I do, eight kilometers shouldn't wear me out."

"Just looking at that track wears me out," he said. "You guys hungry?"

I shook my head. Pete said, "I'll go with you, Al. I wouldn't want you to eat alone."

They walked across to the refreshment stand and I walked down to Mayer's pit to gas with Les Pardee. Chris Tyler was there and Mike Kaprelian. None of them seemed to be looking forward to the afternoon's fun.

"This was big enough for the days of the Rajos and the Frontys," Mike said, "but not for the cars here today."

Chris nodded agreement.

Les said, "Mark used to be king here. He's probably counting his money."

I shook my head. "We ran this track in second gear. And I don't have a second gear now."

"I wish I did," Mike said. "Low speed torque, that's what we need. The straightaways are too short."

We could complain all we wanted to; we were here and we hadn't been brought here in chains. The odds were the same for all of us. We would compete evenly.

Tudi Petrini, who had driven every kind of course open to either two- or four-wheeled vehicles, displayed his all-around class in the first race. He led every lap, taking the checkered flag almost half a lap in front of Harry Shaw.

We were in the second race. The third was open only to the low finishers in the first two. The second didn't seem to have as hot a field as the first race but it was bound to be a crowd pleaser because so many young drivers were in it. There were very few fans who could really appreciate the finesse of a Tudi

Petrini. Wild slides and close finishes, that was what most fans came to see. Petrini was popular because he won. If he had lost with the same technique, his fan club would have evaporated.

The track was well plowed by the time we lined up for the second race. I was glad we had installed the knobbies. I was even happier halfway through the race.

Both of the early leaders had skidded themselves out of contention by that time; it was unlikely they could work their way back through the traffic. Chris Tyler was driving a smart race at the head of the pack, tailed closely by Dutch Krueger. Yours truly rode an easy third, steady as a cruiser on a calm sea. Those knobs were digging down for deep traction, keeping our line true, our power steady.

In the twenty-second lap, Dutch went too high on the bank as he came out of the backstretch. He almost stalled in the piled dirt as I slid past below. It was like a rerun of my first race; I was chasing Chris Tyler home.

I tried to keep the gap to him constant, figuring to make my move, if any, in the last couple of laps. Then Les Pardee showed to my right. That forced a change in my strategy. I gave the blue lady her head.

Les stayed close, never challenging, never pulling wide to go by, just riding my deck through two wild laps. I had a hunch he was trying to force me high on the bank so he could get past below. The track was too rough to the right of my line to give him the traction he'd need to pass.

I held the groove and held the pace I hoped would make a challenge on my right unsuccessful. But in the third lap Les pulled wide to try it.

Chris Tyler was less than fifty feet ahead of us by now; I could see a traffic jam shaping up. About two minutes later we were in it. Chris and I had the groove, Les hung just off my right rear wheel, eating the dust from Chris that I hadn't already digested.

It was like driving in a fog, my forward vision limited to the deck of Tyler's yellow D-O. Grit rattled off my goggles and stung the unprotected skin of my cheeks. If there was any trouble ahead, only one pair of eyes could see it—Chris Tyler's. Les and I were flying blind.

It was not the way I wanted to drive; I believed in making my own mistakes. I dropped back to where the vision was clearer as Les slid into the spot I had deserted. I now rode third with three laps to go. Ahead, Les was trying to get past Chris.

Chris had about the best sense of pace among the younger drivers, but it looked to me as if both he and Les were crowding their traction limit too far. I stayed out of their dust but not out of contention.

It was a lucky move for me. Chris went wide to lap a tail-ender and that sent Les up into the heavy going of the upper track. He was still trying to fight

84

his way down when I zipped past below. I was once again in second place, chasing Chris Tyler toward the checkered flag.

He beat me to it by twenty feet. He beat me to it—*again*.

"Cool show," Al said. "You got over your peeve, huh?"

"I've a new one," I said. "Chris Tyler."

Al smiled, saying nothing.

"He's good, isn't he?" I asked.

Al nodded. "He's a little more experienced, Mark."

"And a lot more talented," I added.

Al shook his head. "We can't be sure of that, not *yet.*" He handed me the water bottle. "Tired?"

"Not too tired for the windup. Unless you've changed your mind about driving that?"

"Nope. I never liked this track and I like it even less right now. And you can use the experience."

That's what I got out of the windup—experience. That's a kinder word than frustration or humiliation. The good boys were in it, again, the older boys, the boys who were even better than Chris Tyler. Petrini won it when Harry Shaw, who was leading in the last lap, spun up the bank and scraped the fence before regaining control. I finished ninth.

chapter SEVEN

WE HAD A RUSH JOB ON A TRANSMISSION
Monday so Pete and I worked overtime to get it out
that night. And we got to talking about Al again and
how different he was from the way we had figured
him this spring.

"A lot of men who were lead-foots as kids slow up
when they get older," I said. "Those buddies of his
last saw him race when he was younger than we
are."

"He was plenty wild that first Sunday," Pete said.
"I think he's got another angle now."

"What's that?"

"You," Pete said. "Building you into a winner. So
you can go up to the big time with Nowak."

"Why should he want that? He's not my father."

Pete smiled. "I can name you some fathers who
take less interest in their sons than Al does in you."

That was true enough. Ever since my dad had
died and we had moved to town, Al had sort of taken

over. He had even helped Mom get her job at the library; Al's cousin was a county commissioner.

"That might be his angle now," I said, "but it wasn't this spring. Remember how he used to burn when his friends asked him who was going to be his driver?"

Pete nodded. "But he didn't know how good *you* were then. Now, he knows."

I looked at my sharp-tongued friend but he was not smiling. "Sarcastic tonight, huh?" I said.

"'Don't give me that phony modesty," he answered. "Two seconds and a win in your first three races?"

"You're overlooking some of my other finishes— like ninth, yesterday."

"You're young," Pete said. "You're learning. Even Al must realize you're no Petrini. But who is?"

Seven of them had finished closer to Petrini yesterday than I had. I had reason for modesty; there was nothing phony about it.

It was a busy week. I noticed that some of the sports car buffs around the county were bringing their cars to us. Evidently Nowak had been right about racing bringing in new business.

Halloran and Moreno helped out Friday and would run the garage Saturday. We would be leaving early in the morning for Millet, Arizona, hoping to beat the afternoon heat.

The track at Millet was almost pure adobe. This time of the year in that dry, hot climate it might as well be concrete. We wouldn't have any traction problem at Millet unless it rained, and it was too late in the season for rain. We changed the tires and gearing and took off long before the sun was up on Saturday.

Millet was near Phoenix and Phoenix was loaded with new motels. We stayed there Saturday night. It had been a long, hot drive with the trailer but Al bought us a fine dinner and we spent a couple hours in the pool before going in to our air-conditioned rooms.

There was some overcast in the morning when we went out to the track. Both Al and I got in a few rounds in the cool air before the sun finally broke through. The track was what Al figured it would be, dirt in name only. We had the right tires and gearing.

Al ran a couple thirty-eight second laps, which is just a little under ninety-five miles an hour. I ran one 35.6 lap, which is a shade over 101 miles an hour. Neither of us had been crowding the car or the track.

It was like coming to a new world after the heavy, jammed going at Canyon City; there was a lot of joking in the pits and a lot of expectation in the air. Stan Nowak wasn't there but he had sent his former driver (and new pit manager) Roy Gaskin.

"A track like this," Les Pardee said, "will give them a better line on the man they want. Because the man they pick will be driving on hard surface tracks about ninety percent of the time."

"Shrewd thinking," I said. "I hope you do well."

He grinned. "And you better, eh?"

"I'm not in the competition," I said. "I have all the problems I can handle learning to run on dirt."

"Sure," he said.

Why try to convince a man that you're different from him? I didn't argue. I asked, "How's your brother doing?"

"Great," he said. "He just bought himself a new Mercedes. I may wind up pumping gas yet."

"You could do both," I said. "I'll bet half the drivers here pump gas during the week. And the other half run garages."

"That's their problem," he said. "I've got bigger plans. You guys hungry?"

"Not as hungry as you are," Pete said. "But we can always eat. Let's go!"

When we came back to the pit, Roy Gaskin and Gus Mayer were there, gabbing with Al. When Al introduced us, Gaskin said, "I've been hearing about you."

"From my boss?" I asked.

He shook his head. "From mine." He winked. "I heard you were a good influence on Al."

Gus Mayer laughed. I smiled. Al said. "We're part of a team. We're a good influence on each other."

A little joke? A half-joke? The truth, really. There

were times when I was too serious and times when Al was not serious enough. The important third man was Pete, who kept us both in balance. The combination was right and even Mom knew it's the combination that counts.

There would be three thirty-five-mile races and a fifty-mile race today. The way it shaped up, there would be no rookie fields. All of the events paid enough to attract the veterans and a track this hard was not a serious strain on the wrists. The big boys would be able to run in more than one event at full capacity.

So I had some competition beyond Chris Tyler in the opener. Dutch Krueger was in it and Harry Shaw and half a dozen other experienced campaigners.

"Good test," Pete said. "Fast field. Gaskin can get a real line on you."

"Don't remind me!"

"Just talking. You'll do all right." He punched my shoulder lightly and went back to the pit.

Harry Shaw flanked me. There were old hands in the row ahead and the row behind. Tyler and Mike Kaprelian seemed to be the only other young drivers in the race.

I saw a lot of both of them in the next thirty-five miles, mostly of Chris. Shaw and Krueger were fighting for the lead after three laps; the rest of us fought our private battles behind them.

I passed Nystrom in the fifth lap without fuss. Mike Kaprelian answered my challenge in the eleventh. Mike didn't have the engine in front of him that I had and he was no more experienced. But he planned to be a career man in this trade and he knew that Gaskin was watching. He carried us into a pace I didn't care to match at this stage of the race. I dropped back for elbow room.

I kept him in sight for three laps with no challenge from behind. I was riding seventh at the time without strain to me or the Nowak. Then Chris Tyler came up from behind.

I answered Chris' challenge as Mike had answered mine. Only this time I was in the front car and Chris had the outside route. We kept the fans happy for lap after lap, creeping closer to Kaprelian. Mike finally felt the heat from behind and increased his own speed. That meant that all three of us were closing in on Manchester.

It was less fun for the drivers than it was for the fans—but it *was* a challenge, trying to figure the strategy against three competitors. And challenge was the reason we were out there.

Among the uninformed, Chris Tyler would have been voted the least likely to come out of the four-car tangle in front. Chris would have to take the long route past three cars to do it.

Kaprelian and Manchester had been rubbing hubs

for two laps; I tailed them closely enough to take advantage of any slides. If Chris got past me, he would have even less track for his next challenge.

He must have been thinking the same way. He didn't make his move until the duel ahead had been settled and we were all back to our grooves. He made his move about three seconds before I decided to make mine. He was abreast and going by when I decided the time was right.

It happened in the backstretch. He was on Mike's deck as Mike and Manchester started the swing around the north turn. He took a different line into the turn than they did and it must have been a better one. Because he came out of it lower on the track than either of them and he zoomed past them before they reached the pit area.

Yours truly now rode eighth, the blackboard informed me. As if I didn't know it!

On a track this firm, in a car like the Nowak, it was not the right place for a man to be this late in the race. I began to move up once again on Mike Kaprelian.

He was still crowding Manchester, and Duke overreacted to the threat in the south turn. He went high on the bank and there was room below. There was room for both of us—and now Manchester was riding eighth.

Both Mike and I had come out of the turn under full control and the Nowak did the rest. We went past in the backstretch and Mike was riding seventh. Ahead, the yellow D-O piloted by Chris Tyler was disappearing into the north.

That blob of yellow gleaming in the sunlight ahead became a personal target. Among the young drivers, Chris was the only man who had beaten me consistently. I almost accepted the fact that he was a better driver. But I felt I had the better car and enough edge in the combination to take him. I went up to try.

Red Nelsen was pulling into the pits as I came sliding into the grandstand lane. My blackboard again told me what I knew; I rode fifth. Soon, I hoped, it would be fourth.

There were only six laps left in the race. Dutch Krueger, Gus Mayer and Harry Shaw were running one, two, three. Petrini wasn't in it. Krueger, Mayer and Shaw might be too much for me but today I was out to prove that Chris Tyler wasn't.

How many times had Al warned me not to make it personal? How many times had he told me to compete with myself? Not often enough evidently; I was determined to take Tyler.

There was no animosity in it. No rational man could dislike Chris Tyler. And no informed man could doubt his skill. But I owed it to the Nowak, I told myself, to prove that our combination was better.

He had a 300-foot lead on me in the twenty-ninth

lap. I cut it to 100 feet two laps later. Ahead of us, Dutch Krueger blew a tire and just managed to get the car under control and into the pit area. Chris and I were now competing for third place, a very respectable finish in this field.

I was moving at a speed faster than I had ever moved before on an oval track but there was no loss of traction, no uncontrolled slides. And I was gaining; the engine in our blue lady was proving to be the difference.

We blasted down on the white flag nose and nose, Chris still on the inside, still holding the short route. Shaw and Mayer were now almost half a mile ahead and nobody was coming up from behind. We had a clear field for our last lap battle.

I had the car and the determination. Chris had the skill and the shorter route. He moved past me in both turns and stayed almost even with me in the backstretch. He came out of the last turn with the nose of his D-O a few feet in front. The Nowak made it up in the dash to the flag, made it up *exactly*. We finished in a dead heat for third place.

"I think you beat him," Pete said. "An electric eye would have proven it. Those judges had a bad angle."

The judges' stand was right on the finish line. I smiled. "I'm happy. He didn't beat me. He had the inside track and he didn't beat me—for a change."

"Don't make it personal," Al said.

"It's not," I said. "Not any more. It's over."

That could have been the high point of the day. But I must admit that Al furnished the high point for the team in the fifty-mile feature run. He had a new approach that day, a blend of the risk-taking attitude we had feared this spring and the steady caution of his later performances.

He took a few risks but none that could be called foolish. He took them all at strategic times and soared into the last ten miles in fifth place, still easily within striking distance of the leader. The leader at the time was Tudi Petrini and nobody in the pits or the stands expected that Al would take *him*.

As it worked out, he didn't take Petrini. But he fought his way to third place, finishing only a car length behind Gus Mayer. And Gus finished less than a car length behind Petrini. It was the closest finish of the day and sent the fans home almost as happy as we were.

chapter EIGHT

WE NEEDED THE CHARGE OF THOSE TWO third-place finishes to carry us through the rough week of work that started Monday morning. Halloran and Moreno were needed full time all week; Al, Pete and I worked overtime.

The main body of it was standard repair work brought in by Al's regular customers and a lot of pre-vacation engine tuning. But three sports cars had been brought in. Their owners evidently didn't trust the foreign car dealer garages which were run mostly on snob appeal and priced accordingly. And then there were the kids from sixteen to sixty who wanted more carburetors, higher compression and hotter ignition on their production specialty cars, the Camaros and Mustangs and Firebirds. The dealer garages could have done as good a job as we did with these; it was about as complicated as changing the sprocket on a bicycle. But they brought their cars to us.

"Why?" Pete asked. "The dealers have all the parts handy and plenty of mechanics."

"They notice the sports cars are coming in here," I guessed. "Maybe they figure we can turn a Firebird into a Ferrari."

"They can't be that dumb," Pete said. "Some of the young ones aren't dumb at all."

"The young ones probably used to watch you and Joe and me at the drags. They're loyal."

"What about the old ones?"

"They're dumb," I said.

Al was standing nearby, taking it all in. "Keep your tongue off my generation," he said. "Most of those old coots aren't as dumb as you guys would like to think they are."

"Yes, boss," I said.

"Right, chief," Pete said.

"And young or old, dumb or bright," Al said, "they're all customers. Let us not forget that! If a man has enough trust in us to bring us his most valuable moveable possession, we owe him our best —in work *and* manners."

We nodded and Al went into his corner office.

"I guess we were told," I said quietly.

"What we forget," Pete said, "is that Al was a racing driver for only a little while. This garage has put bread in his mouth for twenty-three years."

And furnished us a playpen all through high

school, I thought. *And now keeps four of us employed.*

I put down my wrench and went over to the office where my boss was checking some work sheets. "Hey, Al," I told him, "if I said something wrong, I'm sorry."

"Forget it," he said. "Actually, I wasn't thinking of you."

"Who, then?"

"All those kids you read about and see on TV. All those kids who complain about what a lousy world we left them. I'll grant you we made plenty of mistakes and we'll make more. But there were a few years in my short lifetime when it took a lot of doing to leave you any kind of world at all."

"I know that, Al."

"Good," he said. "Back to work."

When I came back, Pete asked, "Everything okay?"

"I guess. He wasn't talking about us really. He's been reading the papers and watching TV."

Pete nodded. "It's a strange thing, isn't it, how adults think all kids are alike?"

"It sure is," I agreed. "It's almost as strange as our thinking all adults are alike. Well, we'd better get to work on Judge Carney's Mustang."

Judge Carney's Mustang was not hot enough for him so he had brought it in to us. All he wanted was about 100 more horses, stiffer suspension, magnesium wheels, competition tires—and whatever else he might see advertised in *Motor Trend* before we had finished. Nothing stick-in-the-mud about Judge Carney; he was only seventy-four.

It was a good thing we weren't racing out of the state this Sunday because we worked straight through until midnight on Saturday, cleaning everything up.

San Valdesto was this week's battleground and that was only a couple of hours away. There would be four of us driving up next morning; Mom had decided she needed another Sunday in the sun.

"That's some switch for you," I said at breakfast. "I thought you didn't approve of Al's favorite sport."

"He asked me to watch it," she explained. "I'm trying to be fair."

"Fair? You don't have to like racing. Al's a tolerant man."

"Don't argue with me. I'm going. One of you boys will have to sit in the back of the truck."

There was room for only three in the seat of the pickup. I tossed for the third seat with Pete and lost. So I sat among the tires and wheels, the water, fuel and oil cans in the box of the truck. It was a hard seat, but I was surrounded by the blended smells of my trade, my favorite perfume.

The San Valdesto surface was not up to Millet's in hardness but it was still a firm track with the steepest bank on the circuit. Before the days of the board tracks, several world record one-mile laps had been established and broken here.

The refreshment stands would not get our money today. Mom had packed a whole thermal chest full of fried chicken and pilaff. It would be sort of like a picnic, with the dust substituting for the ants.

I think she enjoyed it—before the racing started. The crowd and the noise and the gleaming cars were a bright change from the library, and Al brought all of his friends over to be introduced. As the only lady in the infield, she got a lot of attention.

Then, in a trial lap, Red Nelsen slid up the steep bank and bounced off the fence in the north turn, and some of the magic went out of it for Mom. She had been standing in the box of the truck, where she could see the whole track; she went to sit in the cab.

"A mistake," Al said. "I shouldn't have suggested it."

I shrugged.

He sighed. "A guy could slip playing tennis, too, right? He could break a leg."

I nodded. "And think of all the guys who have been hit by golf balls."

A pause. Then Al said, "We're being silly, huh?"

"I'm where I want to be," I said. "I'm doing what I want to do. I'm not putting bullets into deer or sharp hooks into fish or knocking another man down so my buddy can run across a chalk line with a ball. I'm not ashamed of being where I am or doing what I'm doing."

He stared at me. "You sound steamed!"

I said nothing, having said it all.

"I'm older," he said.

"You're still you. That's been good enough for forty-three years. Why change now?"

He sighed again. "Let's get a push. I want to try out the track."

A couple men from Harry Shaw's pit came over to help push him into action and old-young Al Duncan went singing into the south turn. I poured a glass of lemonade from the thermal jug and took it over to Mom.

"You look grim," she said. "Did you and Al have words?"

"Friendly words," I said. "I'm worried about you. It's going to be dusty and boring here in the infield. I can get you a box seat."

"I'd look dumb, sitting in a box seat and reading," she said. "I brought some magazines."

Silence.

"Don't fret," she said. "I'm not going to be a problem. You go on about your business."

It was a sport, not a business, but it wasn't the right time to quibble about that. I went over to where Pete was talking to Les Pardee and Mike Kaprelian.

"How's Red's car?" I asked.

"Okay," Mike said. "Dented, but ready to go. That was close, huh?"

"It spoiled the afternoon for my ma," I said. "She's going to catch up on her reading."

"It's a bad show for women," Mike said. "My girl wouldn't even go to drags. And they're about as dangerous as dancing."

"Drags?" Les said. "You haven't run in a drag for three years."

"I know," Mike said. "But there was cycle racing after that and then jalopies. That's why she's still my girl, not my wife. Well, unless Nowak wants me, wedding bells will soon be ringing."

"Nowak?" Les said. "Mark and Chris Tyler are fighting that fight. The rest of us have been lapped."

"Not yet," Mike said. "Not yet!"

When Mike went back to his pit, Les said, "Personal, maybe? Nervous, Mark?"

"Not yet," I said. "Not yet."

"Your boss sure fooled everybody last Sunday, didn't he?"

"Even me," I admitted. "I'm learning not to underrate him."

"Gus told me that most of the gang think your boss is the best mechanic in the state. He told me that in the old days your dad used to do most of the driving."

"Al's a good man with the wrench," I said. "He's a lot of other things, too. I guess we all are."

"I just want to be one thing," Les said. "I just want to be the man behind the wheel."

He was only one of millions. The country was full of kids who just wanted to be the man behind the wheel. Some outgrew it and some didn't live long enough to outgrow it. I liked the whole car, not just the driver's seat. Even jockeys knew the most beautiful thing about a horse was not the saddle.

We pulled a switch this week; Al drove the opener. He claimed his big effort last Sunday plus the past week's labor at the garage had taken too much out of him; he didn't have enough left for today's sixty-five-mile windup.

I thought he was doing it for me, so I could get more experience over the longer route. But the opener convinced me he'd been telling the truth. In a slow field he was one of the slowest. Last Sunday he had battled the headliners right down to the final flag; today he was being passed by kids in conversions.

As we watched from the pit, Pete said, "Maybe he's trying to show your ma how safe this game can be."

"Maybe," I said. "Or maybe he told the truth. He's had a heavy week."

"So have you," Pete said. "And the way it's shaping up, you'll get your rest today."

"Talk English, amigo."

"Al's riding seventh. Only the first five cars qualify for the windup."

"He's still got a few laps to go. If he doesn't climb up to fifth I can still enter the second race."

"That would give you a ninety-mile day. Ready for that?"

"I'm ready to try. But maybe I won't have to. Al's making his move."

The blue lady was creeping up on a local rocker-arm in the backstretch now; she moved past before they reached the north turn. Our boss rode sixth. We so informed him as he stormed past the pit.

Les Pardee was breezing along in fifth place, well out of fourth place but almost a quarter of a lap in front of Al. There were only three more laps to the checkered flag; it was beginning to look like I had a ninety-mile day ahead. Al was gaining on Les but not at a rate that would close the gap in time.

As it turned out, he never got past Les. He didn't need to. Another local rocker-arm, in third place, blew a hose connection a lap later and Al finished fifth.

That put me into the sixty-five-mile finale with the stars of the first three acts. Most of them had qualified their own cars, which meant they had twenty-five miles of fatigue already stored in them. But they were conditioned men; at least four of them had driven five hundred miles without relief in their long

104

careers—at Indianapolis. And I had a week of overtime behind me.

The above might sound like an alibi. I don't need any. I did all right that day at San Valdesto, while Roy Gaskin watched and Mom read her magazines.

I didn't get rich, but I learned a few things. I watched the lines of a number of drivers into and through the turns, for instance. I watched them from behind, the best vantage point. I saw the different techniques they used in passing me, some on the inside, some on the outside, some on the stretches and some on the turns. I saw the quality and quantity of their dust.

This was all educational but not stimulating. I decided, in the thirty-fifth lap, I had learned enough for one afternoon. I decided to take advantage of my education.

I was less tired after that. The spur of competition started the adrenaline flowing and the response of the Nowak told me she had shared my impatience. We moved up to enjoy the company of our peers.

They did not immediately accept us as equals. A few of them were very stubborn about it, the first being Arnie Terring. Arnie had made the switch to the WDTA in the middle of the season, after campaigning without success in the USAC all spring.

I'm sure he expected to do better here than he had in the established league and his plans probably didn't include being passed by rookies.

One thing I had noticed about Arnie in my previous view from the rear was that he had a tendency to back off early when he rode the inner lane in a duel and a third car would come in sight ahead. He must have had a *thing* about being boxed.

We kept him busy for three laps before the deck of Tom Hayworth's Chev loomed in the dust ahead. I anticipated Arnie's reaction. Though we were bearing down on the north turn, I bottomed *before* Arnie backed off. I was well past him and still in control when we hit the turn.

I was riding on marbles now, high on the steep bank, but the Nowak kept her footing. We stayed even with Hayworth all through the turn and moved past before we reached the first pit.

Passing two cars in a third of a lap rebuilt my confidence. It was clear to me that Dutch Krueger, batting along only a few hundred feet ahead, was going to be our next victim.

His car, I'd noticed, was a little skittery on this surface; my best bet would be to take him on one of the turns. I made the try in the fortieth lap as we streaked past the stands. He went into the turn in his usual slot but at a speed higher than he would have if he wasn't being challenged.

Despite the steepness of the bank his deck began to swing early, as I had guessed it would. I made my move before this happened, going high on the bank, above and behind him. When his slide came I was already turned downtrack. My right foot did the rest. I came out of the turn in front and going away.

So that was one thing I had learned that Sunday afternoon; the smart move is the move you can make *before* your opponent makes his. It requires some educated guessing to be successful. A perfect racing engine reacts quickly to the opening of the throttle but no engine reacts immediately. Men who set records may race against the clock but men who win races must race against men and their machines.

Passing Dutch had brought me up to the men who had learned long ago much more than I had learned that afternoon. So the going from then on was rougher. The superiority of the Duncan-tuned Nowak was now my only edge.

It took me past Manchester and Kaprelian. It brought me up to Chris Tyler. I had my first glimpse of him in the dust ahead as the lady and I completed our sixty-second lap.

I had a closer glimpse a lap later, finishing the sixty-third lap. I picked up even more yardage in the next, the final, two laps but not quite enough. He beat me out of fourth place by 100 feet.

chapter **NINE**

MONDAY WAS A GLOOMY DAY, BOTH AT THE breakfast table and at the garage. According to Pete, Al and Mom had not had much to say to each other on the trip home and I guess they were both still sulking, as adults will.

I kept my mouth shut and my hands busy at the garage. There was plenty to do and Al didn't like any static around him when he was in a mood. We were usually a cheerful group because we had come together by choice, not by accident, but that Monday we could have been working in a big city production garage. The contrast showed me how lucky we all were to be working here.

At lunch, Joe Moreno said, "You guys didn't do so well yesterday, I'll bet."

"We did all right."

"Why is Al so owly, then?"

"Personal reasons," I said.

Pete smiled. I concentrated on my sandwich. Joe

108

said, "The way I heard it, you won't be with us long."

"What way did you hear it?"

"I saw Bill Pardee down at Laguna yesterday. His brother told him you might be driving for Stan Nowak next year."

I said nothing.

"Is that why Al's owly?" Joe persisted.

I shook my head.

"Don't pry, Joe," Pete said. "And don't believe everything you hear. Chris Tyler's got that Nowak job sewed up. Right, Mark?"

"Not yet," I said. "Not yet."

Don't make it personal. Compete only with yourself. That sounded sensible enough but it wasn't easy for anyone who lived in a competitive world. In the last three years of his contract with Stan Nowak, according to the *Racing News,* Roy Gaskin had earned over $70,000 a year. That had to make the job a golden goal for every young driver in the WDTA. Every one of the front runners was bound to be aware of the others. And that made it personal.

Al's mood lightened as the week went on, and Mom, too, began to smile again. I didn't ask either of them why, not being of a temperament to examine the teeth of gift horses. And then, too, maybe I wouldn't understand their reasons because of the generation gap. Let's be honest—I didn't want to remind Mom that I was in the same sport she and Al were arguing about.

We would be going back to Arizona this week but not to Millet. We would be going to the higher country, to Pinecrest. That was cooler country than the Millet-Phoenix area, though no place in Arizona is really cool in summer.

The weather would be hot but the competition would be cooler. Neither Tudi Petrini nor Chris Tyler would be making the trip. Tudi would be at the Riverside Road Races as a factory representative (and vice-president) of the Shivler Carburetor Company. Chris would be attending his sister's wedding.

"That ought to put us up to fourth instead of fifth," Al said.

"Let's not judge by last Sunday," I said. "It wasn't our best day of the season."

"That's for sure." He shook his head irritably. "That was a bad day all around." Another pause. "We'll be leaving Saturday morning. Joe and Red should be able to handle the garage."

What he'd called the "bad day all around" evidently hadn't changed his attitude; he'd be driving again this Sunday. And Mom must have accepted the decision because she made us a raft of turkey sandwiches to eat on the road.

Pinecrest, like most dirt tracks, had originally been built for horse racing. In the big population centers most of these tracks had been converted to hard surface. In the medium population centers

110

many of them had remained dirt but had been banked steeper to accommodate the centrifugal force of racing automobiles on turns. Pinecrest, according to Al, still had the original grade.

Kroyflex had come up with a new tire he thought would be right for this kind of track, neither knobby nor edge-ridged, but grooved longitudinally, as many front tires were on rear drive, front engine cars. We stopped at the garage on the way to pick them up.

"I'm glad Mark's ma packed the turkey," Pete commented. "Those tires must have cost plenty. You probably haven't any money left for hamburgers."

"They cost more than we're likely to win today," Al admitted. "But we all agreed some time ago that we're not in this business for the money. Or didn't we?"

Pete sighed. "We did. At least we're not in *this league* for the money. Mark, now . . ."

"Let's get 'em loaded," I said. "The sun will be up soon."

Pete laughed. "Easy does it. I know you're looking forward to a race without Tyler but there's plenty of time."

Words bubbled in me but I said nothing. He could have been right.

We had a break in the weather. The early morning overcast didn't clear up until noon and we were through the hottest part of the desert long before that. We rolled into Pinecrest in plenty of time to get rooms in the most popular motel, in plenty of time to get unwound before Sunday.

Most of the regulars had made the trip but it wasn't quite the same without our junior ace, Tyler, and our senior ace, Petrini. That left only mere mortals for us to measure ourselves against.

Next morning we ran about a dozen laps with the tires that were on the car and then changed to the new Kroyflex skins. The clock showed us the new tires were better on this track. The difference was less than a second per lap but the difference between first and fourth place was quite often even less than that.

Les Pardee was an unhappy lad at Pinecrest. With Petrini out of the competition, Gus Mayer had decided it was an opportune time for him to pick up some seasonal points on the king. Gus would do all the driving for his stable today.

Al was not in any point race; I would drive the windup. It was the second week in a row that he had decided to limit his driving to the shorter early race. This time he didn't offer any reason.

"I think he's trying to wean himself," Pete said. "I think he plans to cut himself down to no driving at all."

That could be. And it could be the reason Mom had been smiling more since Tuesday. If it was true,

I didn't approve. But Al was a big boy; he could make his own decisions.

"If he stops driving," Pete went on, "and you go to work for Nowak, what about me? What am I going to do next summer?"

"Go to Europe," I suggested, "like Larry Beam. You could stand a little continental polish. Let's go down and heckle Pardee."

Les and Mike Kaprelian were in Arnie Terring's pit, talking about the USAC which Arnie had deserted. There would be more drivers making the switch, according to Arnie. The big winners on the hard surface tracks were all company financed. The WDTA seemed to be the last refuge of the individual owner and driver.

"Even the young ones remember the dirt," he said. "And even the champs will admit it's a better test of a man's skill."

"Maybe," Les said. "But I'll go where the money is."

Mike nodded agreement.

"I've been there," Arnie said, "and got very little of it. Good luck to you. I think there's more fun here."

It could have been a loser's philosophy. Except that Petrini and Shaw and Mayer and a few others had made the same decision, men who had been winners on every surface in the country.

From our pit, Al called, "If you guys have finished your social hour, I could use a push."

Pete sighed. "Back to the world of reality. Coming, boss!"

Engines whining, dust drifting, mechanics and drivers joking—reality was too harsh a word for it. *Living,* maybe, but I guess living is reality.

Competition is certainly reality. Good or bad humored, the man in the other car is out to beat you. We all understood that and accepted it. As I've mentioned too often before, the danger is in making it personal. But I still wished Chris Tyler was here.

Al, so far as I knew, had no targets in the opening field, not before the green flag dropped. After that they would become personal in the order in which he passed or was passed by them.

There were more than the usual number of stars in the opener; Gus Mayer wasn't the only veteran who hoped to pick up points on Petrini. Shaw and Mayer were in the first row, Mayer on the pole. They had to be the favorites. Dutch Krueger and Red Nelsen were in the second row, Al was flanked by Arnie Terring in the third. There were three more rows behind them with only one local driver in the field.

If Al had plans to retire from the driving end of this sport, it would be logical to guess he would just go through the motions today, stay out of trouble, try only to qualify the car for the windup.

114

He started in fifth place and never dropped below sixth. The four men in front of him had a big edge in experience. Al's leverage was the Nowak engine and those Kroyflex tires. For seven rugged laps he fought off the challenge of Arnie Terring behind the duels of the point-hungry quartet ahead. Then, when they began to run into the heavier dust of the leaders, Al backed off and Arnie moved into fifth place.

Arnie had transferred too late in the season to think about points; he was out for the first place money. Al kept him in range as the dust grew heavier and the traction looser. It was a twenty-five-mile race and Al was still hanging close in the twelfth lap when Arnie came charging up on the offset Chev of Red Nelson.

Red's car wasn't moving at its early speed, though she seemed to be firing okay. Arnie zipped past him just before the grandstand turn. That sent him high on the shallow bank.

And our boss pulled the play of the day with a line into the turn that put him above Red and below the sliding Arnie. It was a gutty move, an unexpected move—and it paid off. He came into the lane in fourth place and under full control.

"Hey, hey!" Pete said. "Is that our Al out there?"

"I guess he's not going to retire," I said. "He's getting better, isn't he?"

"He understands cars," Pete said. "And especially that one."

That was his strength. The great ones had a great touch, an instinct. Al had a fair touch—and a lot of knowledge. He didn't *sense* the load he was putting on an engine or the strain he was putting on his tires, he *knew*. He had driven every kind of car manufactured in America on every kind of road the country offered. He would never make any drivers' hall of fame but he knew as well as anybody alive what an engine would do and what it should do.

The three still in front of him, Mayer, Shaw and Krueger, had natural talents Al couldn't match and their early pace had put them out of reach of the Nowak's superiority. Al took the checkered flag where he had finished the twelfth lap, in fourth place.

He came in looking unhappy. "I should have stayed up there earlier," he complained. "I let them get too big a gap."

"This time," I said. "But not next time. Live and learn, drive and improve."

The unhappy look was replaced by an uncomfortable look.

"Right, boss?" I said.

"Don't heckle me," he said. "Where's my glass of water?"

"Right here," Pete said, and handed him one. "That was some move you made on Red and Arnie. You looked like Petrini."

"I'm not Petrini," he said. "I never was." He

116

drank the water and climbed out wearily. "But I guess I've shown a few of my contemporaries I'm not quite the fool they thought I was."

"Al," I said, "remember what you told me—don't make it personal!"

"I don't have to," he answered. "Not any more. I'm a mechanic and I know it. But I can still beat the mechanics who think they're drivers." He went slowly over to the truck to put his helmet away, to rinse off his face.

"What's he bitter about?" Pete asked.

"I don't think he is," I said. "I think he's got a new picture of himself, about halfway between what he dreamed he was and what Tom Winter, Stan Nowak and Jack Belmont claimed he was."

"Wouldn't that make him bitter?"

"Adjusted," I corrected him. "Sometimes it's hard to tell them apart."

"You mean resigned?"

"At our age, it's resigned. At Al's age, it's adjusted."

"It's too complicated for me," Pete decided. "Is there any of that turkey left?"

There were three sandwiches left so we each had one, along with some of Mom's homemade pickles.

"Your ma's a great cook," Al said.

I nodded. Pete smiled.

"And a wonderful woman," Al added.

Pete smiled. I nodded.

"Aagh, you kids!" he said. "Let's get to work."

We checked over the Nowak and watched the finish of the second race. We watched the third race all the way through and then it was time for our lady's second appearance of the day.

"Should be a breeze for you," Pete said. "Tyler can't take you today."

"There are at least a half-dozen men here who can drive better than Chris Tyler," I told him.

Pete started to answer, but Al said, "That's enough of *that*." He looked at me. "You drive your own race, understand? You're not dumb. You know what you can do and what you can't do. It's no time for kid stuff."

I nodded.

Pete said, "Luck, Mark."

I nodded again and winked at him. The engines were turning, the starter watching. These were all the winners. Al was right in a way—it was no time for kid stuff. When you play with the men, you'd better be one.

I said, "Pete was just kidding me, Al."

"I know, I know!"

"Chris Tyler is no more personal to me than your —your contemporaries are to you."

"So, okay, I get the message. So I worry too much about you. I keep remembering this was all my idea. You wouldn't even be here, except for me."

118

"I wouldn't be a lot of things, except for you, Al. Don't let Mom panic you."

He answered something but I couldn't hear his words. The starter was waving us on and all the engines began to growl at the same time as we edged forward for the flying lap.

Two weeks ago, at Millet, Al and I had taken two thirds. Last week, at San Valdesto, we had taken two fifths. If the pattern stayed constant, I was due for a fourth-place finish today. Fourth in this field was nothing to be ashamed of but I hoped to do better. The new tires had been a perfect choice for this track and the Nowak was perking like a dream in the light air.

Dutch Krueger had the pole and he set a stiff pace around toward the green flag. With its present gearing, Dutch's car didn't have great low speed torque; he was running at a speed that would give him the best chance at the jump-off. That was one of the advantages of being the pacemaker.

The Nowak and I were in the second row behind Dutch and Gus Mayer. Shaw had the rail in our row. Al had fallen too far behind this same trio in his race. It was a mistake I hoped to avoid.

Dutch's strategy had been sound; he grabbed the lead at the flag as Gus rode his deck into the first turn. I stayed even with Shaw through the turn and moved ahead of him as we broadsided out into the backstretch. I was running third and running easy; it looked like the beginning of a happy race.

Dutch and Gus fought quite a battle, a real crowd pleaser, for five laps. I kept them in sight, still riding third, while Harry Shaw made no move to take me but stayed close enough to let me know he was there.

The field was already scattering, each driver trying to find the gait that would give him his best chance in the forty-five miles left with the equipment he was driving. There was no sense of strain in the Nowak; I stayed within sight of the leaders.

Dutch finally got the edge on Mayer in the seventh lap. Harry Shaw came up behind me to make his bid in the ninth. With forty-one miles still in front of us, I offered only a token resistance. He moved into third place in the twelfth lap.

I was now riding in the spot where the boss had finished, but I didn't stay in the pattern long. Dutch Krueger's Offy coasted into the pits, trailing smoke, and I was back to third. Shaw moved up to tangle with Mayer for the lead.

My confidence grew; I moved up to keep them both in sight and there was still no feeling that I was extending the Nowak or crowding the edge of her almost perfect traction. If there were really "horses for courses," I was riding the right horse for this course today.

Judging by the noise of the crowd, Shaw and Mayer must have been fighting a fierce battle for the top spot. But our blackboard confirmed what I could see with my eyes—they weren't picking up any ground on me. I kept a loose rein on the lady, waiting for the duel ahead to be decided.

They were still fighting in the twenty-fifth lap. Nobody had come up from behind; evidently we were moving fast enough to discourage any challenges. According to the board I had a half-mile lead on the fourth place car.

Knowing what could happen at this speed was the only thing that kept the running from being dull for me at this stage. The leaders were a quarter of a lap ahead, my nearest contender half a lap behind. This was supposed to be a race, not an exhibition. I loosened the rein a little to get a closer look at the pair in front of us.

I could tell by the lines they were forced to take into the turns that their traction wasn't up to the Nowak's, not today. I moved up close enough to let them know they were no longer alone.

Mayer had the temporary edge, the inside track. Shaw wasn't crowding him, hanging about twenty feet off Mayer's deck, waiting for a tactical error, a soft spot, any small break that would give him his chance. There were plenty of laps left and Harry Shaw was a patient man.

It wasn't likely this track would develop any soft spots and even less likely that Gus Mayer would make a tactical mistake. But, despite my superior traction, it was least likely of all that rookie Mark Devlin could take both these veterans at the same time. I hung back out of the heaviest dust but still within range.

The laps rolled on and my patience grew thin and the situation ahead didn't change. I was driving well within my skill; if Gus or Harry had been out in front alone, I could have made my move easily. I tried to keep cool and calm and cunning.

Shaw finally made his bid in the forty-first lap, pulling even in the backstretch, pulling slightly ahead, trying to maintain his edge into the turn. He still had the outside track and I knew he had finally misjudged his traction limit.

My right foot went down as he entered the turn. I caught the slot just right and stayed under control— as Shaw's D-O went broadsiding up the shallow bank toward the fence.

I came past the grandstand in second place and there were still nine laps left to take Gus Mayer. I had the engine, the traction, the desire.

There was really only one thing I lacked—the skill. I realized now that Gus had been breezing and that was why it had been so easy to keep him in sight. He drove to win, not to set records. He paced himself against the competition, not the clock.

I chased him for nine laps and finished second by thirty feet. It was frustrating but also enlightening. I learned (from the rear) how a master stays in front.

chapter TEN

I'D HAD THE BEST EQUIPMENT IN THE FIELD.
Petrini and Tyler had not been present. Gus Mayer
had beaten me to the checkered flag. But one comforting fact remained—I'd taken a second in the
feature at Pinecrest!

And though we weren't here for the money, our
total purse, including Al's fourth, paid for the trip
and the tires and left a few surplus dollars for the
hamburger fund. The ride home didn't seem nearly
as long as the ride down.

Though it was almost two in the morning, Mom
was still up, watching the late, late, late show on the
boob tube. Mom didn't care much for any television
program; the antique western she was watching
could have been a new low.

"You were worried," I guessed.

"What makes you think that?"

I looked at the image on the tube and back at
her.

"Okay," she said, "maybe I was worried. I had a

nap this afternoon and wasn't very tired. How did everything go?"

"I took a second in the big race. Al took a fourth in the qualifier. We made more money than we spent."

"Is this the first time you didn't lose money?"

"I don't know. It might be. What are you worried about, Mom?"

"A world I don't understand," she answered. "A man's world."

"You're not being specific."

"Neither is my worry," she said. "I think of my boy, going two hundred miles an hour at Indianapolis. I think of Al, who won't grow up." She shrugged.

I said, "Nobody goes two hundred miles an hour at Indianapolis and Pinecrest is not Indianapolis. Who's been talking Indianapolis to you?"

"Joe Moreno's mother. I met her in the supermarket yesterday. She said that Joe told her that if you got this job with Mr. Nowak, you could earn as high as a hundred thousand dollars a year."

"We have a rule of thumb on Joe Moreno," I explained. "We believe about a third of everything he says."

"Does that mean you'd get thirty-three thousand dollars a year for driving sixty-six miles an hour at Indianapolis?"

I laughed. She sighed and turned off the set, right

124

in the middle of a big gun battle. She said, "You must be awfully tired. I certainly didn't wait up to lecture you. Would you like something to eat?"

"No, thanks. Mom, you're still the boss you know."

She shook her head. "Not if you're what I want you to be. And you are. You're a man, Mark Devlin. Are you getting up early tomorrow?"

"Not as early as usual. Al said I didn't have to come in until nine o'clock."

"That'll give you about six hours of sleep."

"He's a tough boss, that Al," I agreed. "But I'll tell you something else about him: He's a lot more mature than Pete and I thought he was this spring and maybe more mature than you think he is right now."

She smiled. "That wouldn't be difficult. Good night, second-place-winner in the big race. Good night, Luke Devlin's stalwart son."

Mom usually came up with better lines than that, but she'd been watching that TV western.

"Good night, worrywart," I said.

In the morning she was fairly chipper again. She'd made waffles and pork sausages and I had them with a couple eggs and toast, food for a man who was still a growing boy. We talked about everything but racing.

The garage was jumping when I got there at nine o'clock. Everybody was busy and there were four cars waiting to be worked on. It could have been a letdown after our big Sunday but it wasn't. Each car was a separate problem and one of them had an ignition malfunction that had already licked three garages in the county. It didn't lick Al; we had a new lifetime customer.

The load tapered off by Thursday and Al had time to spend on the Nowak. This was different from his other work. He wasn't doctoring the sick; he was trying to make the near perfect more nearly perfect.

"If you'd had just a little more last Sunday," he explained, "you might have taken Mayer."

"A little more in his skull, not under the hood," Pete said. "We need a brain surgeon, Al."

Al played it straight. "No. He may lack experience but his reactions are faster than Mayer's. I think we're going to surprise a lot of people in these last two races."

We would be racing at El Cajon this Sunday and then finish the season with the high point hundred-miler at Linus. El Cajon wasn't more than a couple hours drive; we had a full night's sleep on Saturday.

As we were unloading Sunday morning, Al told me I would drive the feature again. This time I asked him why.

"Why not?" he answered.

"It isn't why you're here, to watch me have fun. This was all your idea; why should I have all the fun?"

126

"I'm having fun," he said. "But maybe I'm older than I thought I was. I could be a lot younger than you guys thought I was but still be too old for the long races."

"You could be," I admitted, "but I don't think you are."

"I am. Watching my car win, that's fun enough for me. Getting it ready to win, that's fun, too."

"Each to his own," Pete explained. "Al gets the car ready, you drive it—and I eat hamburgers. Each member of this team has his own specialty."

"You used to like to race," I said. "You sure drove in a lot of drags."

Pete nodded. "And maybe next year, if you go with Nowak, Al will break me in on this circuit."

"Maybe," Al agreed. "It's not easy to find a driver who'll work for hamburgers." He looked over at the stands, already a quarter filled. "I just want to be here."

Chris Tyler's yellow D-O came loafing into his pit and Pete said, "Let's go down and ask him about the wedding. I can tell him about your second at Pinecrest. I'll be your press agent."

"No time for visiting now," Al said quietly. "I want Mark to try out the track."

I cruised for about half a dozen laps on that first trip. The surface was roughly the same as Pinecrest's but the bank was steeper; it was a faster track. When I came in, Al went out for a few laps.

When he came in he asked, "Any suggestions?"

It was sort of a test, I knew. "The tires?" I guessed.

He nodded. "Those Kroyflex skins aren't for this track. We don't need that much lateral traction. Let's get to work."

We changed all four tires and Al went out again. Three laps later he came in smiling. "Try her," he said.

He was right. The difference in handling was small but noticeable, the forward traction improved. I could feel it now. But he'd known it *before* the change. I should have known it, too; it was strictly within the realm of a driver's judgment.

There wasn't any time for visiting that morning. I wasn't in a mood for it and there was too much to learn on the track. Terring, Mayer and Tom Hayworth came over to eat lunch with us, but the talk was mostly of the old days. Pete and I only listened.

And then it was time for Al to go out and mix with his peers and (incidentally) qualify his protégé for the day's money race. He had a light week of work behind him and a car under him that had been tuned to the teeth. He had a right to look optimistic and he exercised it.

The field was mixed, some rookies, some veterans, two locals. Petrini wasn't in it or Gus Mayer. But Shaw, Tyler and Terring were in it. Al started on the inside of the third row.

128

He got a bad start. The car directly in front of him was a clunker driven by a local and it stuttered and almost stalled about fifty feet past the green flag.

Al had to hit the brakes hard to keep from piling up; five cars slid past him before he could pull clear to get by. Halfway through the first turn he was riding ninth.

"Oh, boy!" Pete said. "I hope he takes it easy."

"How can he? He's in ninth place."

"I mean—I hope he doesn't do anything foolish. I mean—he really had high hopes for this one. Didn't you notice it?"

"Yes. But he's been in ninth place before."

"Not for the same reason," Pete argued. "And besides, it's different now. It's closer to showdown time. He has to qualify you for the windup."

"No, he doesn't."

"He *thinks* he does," Pete said. "And that's the same thing."

"Put it on the board, then," I suggested. "Tell him to take it easy."

Pete stared at me. "You must be crazy! *He's* the boss!"

"That's right. And he hasn't done anything foolish all season. He knows what he's doing and how to do it. Have faith, amigo!"

If Al was annoyed by that dumb first turn tangle, his driving didn't show it. He worked his careful mechanic-driver way up to seventh place in the next two laps, trusting his superior equipment to carry most of the load.

He took Duke Manchester in the fifth lap and moved into company where his equipment alone was not enough. Arnie Terring was the first to offer him a real battle in his climb. Watching the savage way they fought each other, a spectator never would have guessed what friends they'd been at lunch. They threw dirt all over the oval for lap after lap before Al finally found an advantage in the north turn and came broadsiding out in front to stay.

Shaw, Tyler, Krueger and Nelsen were still ahead of him.

"Fifth place," Pete said. "That's good enough."

"Good enough for what?"

"To put you into the windup."

"That's not why he's out there."

"Not completely. But mostly. You're our ace." He went over to chalk a big "5" on the board.

"Keep the eraser handy," I said. "That's not why he's out there."

The flash of yellow in the dust behind Shaw was the D-O of Chris Tyler. Krueger and Nelsen were jousting for third place about 200 feet further back. Al was closing in on all of them, stretching the daylight between him and Terring.

"Twelve laps to go," Pete said. "He's trying to build up a safe edge over Arnie." He held up the board as Al streaked past.

130

Al signaled that he'd seen it—but continued to gain on the leaders. Pete watched him doubtfully.

Nelsen was next. Al crowded him for two laps before making his bid in the backstretch. They were hub and hub into the turn, Red on the inside. Al had the long route but he came out in front and going away.

"You could be right," Pete said. "The boss is really winging!" He erased the "5" on the board and chalked in a big "4".

Shaw, Tyler and Krueger were still leading in that order, Krueger no more than a few hundred feet in front of Al. Our employer began to close in on Dutch as Tyler finally edged ahead of Shaw.

"Your friend Chris is leading the parade," Pete said.

"I have eyes. Get the board ready for Al. Here he comes!"

The Nowak went by, singing in a high soprano, closing in on Krueger. Al was a member of the team but also his own whole man with his individual dreams, much too much his own man to be only a Mark Devlin qualifier. Pete should have known that by now.

Al's battle with Nelsen had been the show of the race; his battle with Dutch Krueger topped it. Al had the car and Dutch had the savvy. If Dutch's mount had matched his touch, he'd have been right up there with Petrini in the point standings. His engine was an

Offy but it was an ancient one and the chassis that housed it was even older. Al dogged him closely, waiting for the inevitable.

Tyler was alone in front now; Shaw was losing ground with every lap. A furlong behind them, Al made his bid in the backstretch. He was in luck; Dutch's car coughed as Dutch bottomed. It was only a split-second pause but that was all the Nowak needed. She went sailing into third place.

Al could have finished higher than that, I'm sure. He was within range of Shaw and Tyler when he came charging up on the same laggard who had stymied him at the start of the race. Shaw and Tyler had lapped him easily but he evidently decided he had been shamed enough. He hogged the stretches and threw up a wild barrage of grit on the turns. A driver who wasn't also a mechanic might have risked his equipment; by the time Al got past him it was too late to catch Tyler and Shaw. Tyler won it.

When Al came in, he asked, "Who was that kid in the rocker-arm?"

"I don't know," I said. "He might have cost you first place, huh?"

Al shook his head. "Not the way Tyler and Shaw were moving. But I shudder to think of what might have happened if some hothead had come up behind him. I'm going down to talk with Mayer and Petrini. Somebody has to give that kid the *word*."

132

"Can't you wait until we congratulate you?" Pete asked.

"Thank you," Al said, "but I've finished third before." He jumped out and headed for Mayer's pit.

"When did he take a third before?" I asked Pete.

"At Millet. And when he was our age, probably. You know, I think he's more worried about what might happen to that kid than what the kid did to him."

I nodded. "We're in good hands, aren't we?"

"The best," Pete said. "Let's get a root beer. I'm thirsty."

"Let's wait for Al," I said.

Roy Gaskin was at the infield refreshment stand, standing with Chris Tyler. "Fine race," he said to Al. "Some engine!"

"It's twice the engine it was this spring," Al admitted. "Where's the boss today, out on the golf course in his wheel chair?"

"In Milwaukee," Gaskin said. "At the two hundred miler. You going to drive the windup, Al?"

Al yawned. "Nope. My ace will handle that. This is a young man's game. Who should know that better than you, eh, Roy?"

We all laughed—including Gaskin. And then he said, "You win, Al. The refreshments are on me."

The race was over; we were all friends again.

The feature finale would be a sixty-five-miler. It

was hot and getting hotter; it would be a dusty show. Petrini won the second sprint, Mike Kaprelian the consolation.

Petrini had set a new track record for one, five, ten, fifteen, twenty and twenty-five miles. He was given a standing ovation as he lined up on the pole in the finale.

There would be fifteen cars fighting for the points and the money in this one, two points a lap to the winner, 130 points to be picked up. But that was only the reward; that came *after* the race was run. The real fun was in the running, the judgment of car, competitors and surface that would bring a man to the front if he could find the proper blend.

Tyler flanked Petrini in the first row, Shaw and Kaprelian made up the second, Mayer and Hayworth the third. The Nowak rumbled quietly to herself on the rail in the fourth row.

That put me roughly in the middle of the pack, where I stayed for ten laps. Usually, after ten miles, the field would be scattered. But it was a tight field today of well matched men and machines. Evidently, nobody was crowding Petrini and that kept the pace down and the traffic crowded.

The Nowak's song was not happy; she didn't relish this no-contest parade. I let her move up to where we could get a closer look at Tom Hayworth's Chev. Tom must have been getting bored, too. The Chev took off.

We had a little show-off room between the leaders and the laggards; we kept our audience interested through four laps before the engineering superiority of the overhead cam four over the rocker-arm eight took final effect and the blue lady eased into sixth place.

The traffic was less crowded now. The five cars in front of us could have been well spread because my board informed me we were a half-mile behind the leader. That was too much gap; we began to narrow it.

Gus Mayer had been in the same starting row with Hayworth so I half expected he would be the next to come into view in the dust ahead. I should have guessed he wouldn't still be there, not with his friend Petrini leading the parade. Mike Kaprelian would be our next opponent.

Mike was not as experienced as Tom Hayworth and his mount was no faster so it should have been an easier victory for us. But Mike knew that Roy Gaskin was watching, so this race was important to him. He already had one first for the afternoon; another high finish could make him the day's leading contender in the Nowak sweepstakes. Tom had his own business and no urge for the big money road.

The show Mike and I put on didn't seem to draw the noise my match with Hayworth had sparked. Evidently there was more excitement for the fans in a battle still in front of us. Petrini and Mayer?

135

Petrini and Tyler? Tyler and Mayer? It didn't matter at the moment; Mike was giving me all the excitement I could handle.

Mike wasn't what you'd call a cool driver but he was a gutty one and he stretched it a little, knowing I had the edge in equipment. It was important to me to get past him, up to the test I wanted to take, the Tyler test, and I had to be careful not to let my impatience force any bad moves.

I took him finally in the thirtieth lap, the lady's superior traction holding me to the shorter route on the grandstand turn. More than half of the race was still to be run and we were in fifth place in a field of winners.

Shaw, Tyler, Mayer and Petrini were still in front, so far as I knew. I hadn't passed them or seen any of them go into the pits. The Nowak's song was happier; we had room to breathe and some stiff challenges ahead.

I caught a glimpse of yellow disappearing around the next turn and wondered if it could be Tyler. It wasn't any of the other leaders; none of them was driving a yellow car. Was it a tail-ender?

Our board informed me it was Tyler. That had probably been Pete's idea, telling me something he thought I might want to know. The glint of yellow stayed constant as a star for three laps, never showing any other color near it. Chris Tyler was riding all alone in fourth place and traveling as fast as I was. I pressed my right foot deeper.

I caught up to him in the forty-third lap and the fireworks started. He had the inside lane, the choice of slots and (maybe) a better touch. He didn't gain a length in four screaming laps and neither did I.

I dropped back out of the contention and out of the dust as we entered the front stretch in the fourth lap of the duel. Shaw and Mayer were waging a war of their own about 300 feet ahead; a four car tangle was something I wanted to avoid, with only eighteen miles to go.

The yellow D-O had also slowed as Chris evaluated the situation ahead. Our relative positions didn't change, just our speed. We rode that way for two more laps before Chris decided to move up and find a route past the pair fighting it out for second place.

I stayed where I was. Nobody was coming up from behind, my pit had told me, and I figured the traction of the Nowak would give me all the leverage I would need when the time was right. This track was already rough and due to get rougher.

This contest I was looking forward to had nothing to do with Roy Gaskin or Stan Nowak or Indianapolis or anything else Joe Moreno and Pardee and Pete had needled me about. I just figured Chris Tyler had beaten me too often. He wasn't older or more experienced enough to overcome the edge I had in equipment, I felt. It may have been personal but it was not emotional; I simply figured my record against him should be better.

I would like to report a stirring head to head duel to the flag, in the interest of dramatic narrative. But it didn't happen that way, though I beat him to the flag.

I was almost all out, trying to catch all three of them in the sixty-second mile, when Chris finally made his desperation bid to get past Mayer and Shaw at the same time.

He tried it in the backstretch and not one of those proud men would back off in the face of the turn coming up. Mayer had the groove and went through unscathed. But Shaw slued higher and his right rear wheel rubbed the left front wheel of the yellow D-O. At that speed, it could have been disastrous.

It wasn't quite that. Both of them went into a gilhooley and came to rest against the fence. Neither was hurt but they were both out of the money in this one. I chased Gus Mayer home and he chased Petrini. Al and I had our pair of thirds for the day.

"You beat him," Pete said.

I shook my head. "Circumstances beat him. I'll have to wait until next week."

"A hundred miles," Pete reminded me.

"I know. I hope business is light this week at the garage."

138

chapter **ELEVEN**

THERE ARE ALL KINDS OF CARS THAT RACE
and all distances are covered. The drag race is standard, 440 yards, one quarter of a mile from a standing start. Sports cars frequently race against a time
limitation, so that many cars are in different laps
when the race is over. Stock car races run up to 400
and 500 miles, while the USAC big car schedule
spans the gamut from sprints to the automotive
Kentucky Derby—the Indianapolis 500 on Decora-
tion Day.

For lovers of the dirt the traditional "big one" had
always been the hundred-miler. It had been the
Fourth of July feature and the Labor Day season-
ender at dirt tracks all over America for fifty years.
Our season-ender would be at Linus this Sunday.
The USAC had the Labor Day booking.

Tuesday, as I was getting ready to go home, Al
called me into his office. "How do you feel about
Sunday?" he asked me. "Think you can go the whole
route or do you want some help?"

139

"You're the boss," I said.

"I'm well aware of that but it has nothing to do with my question."

"I can drive a hundred miles," I said. "That sixty-five last Sunday was a breeze."

"Okay, you'll drive it all, then. I had a phone call from Stan Nowak this morning. He and Gaskin will be there and they'll make their decision then. It's between you and Tyler."

"They're not on our team," I said.

He frowned. "What are you talking about? Who isn't on our team?"

"Gaskin and Nowak. We'll be there to win, won't we, not to impress Gaskin and Nowak. They're all I've been hearing about for weeks. I'm not running in any popularity contest."

He smiled. "You know who you sound like?"

"You, this spring," I guessed.

"Right! You got something against money?"

"I've always had a proper respect for it," I said. "It's the *improper* respect for it that's been bugging me lately."

Al continued to smile. "Now you sound like your father. Well, we'll run our own race Sunday. We'll show 'em, huh?"

"We'll try. I hope Chris Tyler doesn't pull another dumb one. I want to beat him straight out."

"That's where we're different," Al said. "I hope they all pull dumb ones; it makes the winning easier."

The way I figured it, a guy could get mighty hungry waiting around for the good boys in the WDTA to make mistakes. They made them; every driver does occasionally. But the likelihood of Chris Tyler pulling two bonehead plays on successive weeks was almost nil.

We had a surprise customer Thursday morning, Larry Beam in a brand new Jaguar roadster he'd picked up in Europe. Al was out and I was writing up the work sheets.

"I thought I'd bring it in to the experts," he said. "I've been hearing about you, Mark."

"Not in Europe, you haven't. What's wrong with the Jag?"

"Nothing serious. She idles rough. I thought a tune-up wouldn't hurt—and where else would I go for that?"

"No place but here," I admitted. "Good looking car."

He nodded, "Kind of a —bribe."

I stared at him.

"A little joke," he explained. "It's this and Princeton and banking. Or *not* this and Cal Poly and architecture. Get the picture?"

"That car would look out of place at Cal Poly," I said. "I remember you were always good at mechanical drawing."

"You got the picture." He paused. "What would you do, Mark?"

I stared at him again.

"What's wrong?" he asked.

I shrugged. "I never thought I'd live to see the day Larry Beam would ask *me* for advice."

"I'd like an outside opinion," he said quietly. "Most of the guys I hang around with are pretty, well, pretty standard."

"Europe," I guessed. "That gave you a new view."

He nodded. "I suppose."

"I heard a speech once," I said. "The speaker called it 'America, This Way Up.' It was about people doing what they wanted to do and doing it well. Some of the guys thought it was corny. But I didn't. That's about the only answer I can give you, Larry."

He was staring now and his stare lasted longer.

I said, "I'll write it as a general tune-up. We'll give it what it needs and nothing more. You can trust us. You can pick it up at five o'clock."

He was still staring, but not at me. He nodded. "Get it really sharp. I'll probably be selling it."

He went out and Pete came over. "Wasn't that Beam? Is that his car? What'd he want?"

"He wanted a tune-up and a road map," I said. "We'd better let Al work on this one."

"Road map? What does he think this is, a gas station?"

"No, he thought it was the oracle at Delphi. Let's

get to work; you're not getting paid to ask questions."

He laughed. "My, you're a big man when Al's gone! I hope that Tyler cuts you down a couple notches Sunday."

Silly as it sounds, I almost said, "Who's Tyler?" I'd been lost in another world for a few minutes, a world where I'd thought that different people wouldn't have the same problems.

We had enough work for the four of us that week but not so much that anyone had to work overtime. Al spent his evenings putting new wiring and new exhaust valves in the Nowak. We wouldn't have a fuel problem, we decided; the lady was averaging about four miles to the gallon and the tank would carry us the full hundred miles.

I didn't go to bed early Saturday night; I knew I wouldn't sleep without unwinding first. So Pete, Joe and I went to a movie. It was a real laugher about three-armed monsters from another planet who were trying to destroy our civilization with an electronic ray that turned man's blood to water. It was the perfect relaxer.

There was some overcast in the morning when Al came to pick me up. He came early; we needed a few test runs to see if those new valves were seating properly or needed adjustment. We were the first people at the track, except for some kids who didn't want to miss a single minute of the action on this big day.

Al said, "Your pop and I used to ride our bikes here in the old Triple-A days. We'd have to leave home while it was still night in order to make it."

"Permissive parents," Pete commented. "No wonder you guys were so wild."

Al sighed. "Let's get to work. I'm worried about those valves."

I gave them a strong ten-mile test and they were fine, as I knew they would be. Then Al went out, to "keep his touch for next year," as he put it. By the time he came in there were other drivers and mechs in the pits getting ready for their practice runs and the overcast was burning away.

The big white Caddy was parked in the infield and Jack Belmont was making the rounds, greeting old friends and meeting new ones. Out on the track, Mike Kaprelian and Chris Tyler were loafing through the backstretch, while Harry Shaw was pushed to a start at the other end of the pits.

It was point harvest time in the WDTA. Petrini had first place in the standings sewed up but the race for second, third and fourth place was still wide open.

We were eating the breakfast Mom had packed, sweet rolls, orange juice and coffee, when Les Pardee came over.

144

"I've made my decision," he told us. "I'm going to work at the station for my brother."

"A wise decision, everything considered," Pete said.

Les looked at him suspiciously and then at me. "He's buying an Offy. He'll be racing in this league next season." Another glance at Pete. "We'll *share* the driving."

"That should be fun," I said. "Sit down and have a sweet roll."

Some others came over to gab and heckle as the stands began to fill, as the qualifying started. A warm-up lap and two timed laps, with the best of the two counting—that was the qualifying pattern.

Chris Tyler had the fastest lap, until Petrini qualified. And then it was time for yours truly.

The sun was out and the Nowak was ready. I didn't loaf but neither did I take any chances. I cut a thirty-six-second lap and figured that should put us in one of the first three rows. It earned us the rail in the third row.

Tyler, Shaw, Petrini and Gus Mayer were in the rows ahead. Arnie Terring flanked me. Jack Belmont was adding a little tone to the season's finale; we had a Cobra pace car.

All the engines were turning over. Al said, "Luck!" Pete patted my shoulder. They went back to the pit. The starter signaled and the Cobra edged forward. The beginning of the end was under way.

The dust was light, the track firm, the start clean. Tyler and Petrini opened a gap with the drop of the flag, slugging it out for the lead in the first turn. Jack Belmont had added something besides the pace car today; there would be lap money.

Mayer and Shaw rode in tandem ahead. Terring decided to go up and mix with them. I let him go, steering clear of any early traffic jams. I had started in fifth place and now rode sixth, with no immediate threat from behind.

We batted along in sixth place for three laps, for four, for five. Either the boys behind were playing it cool or there were a lot of engines not working to their potential. At the end of the fifth lap, my board informed me, I had a quarter of a lap advantage over the seventh place car and was only an eighth of a lap behind Harry Shaw, riding fifth.

The Nowak was steady as a cruiser and unless my sense of pace and my tachometer had both gone sour at the same time this was too slow a pace for *any* stage of the race. I went up to get a closer look at Harry Shaw.

He was alone. There was no car within sight in front of him, though the entire backstretch was in view. It was possible the boys in front of him were already running away from the field. The black-board hadn't mentioned *that*. I moved up to make my bid in the front stretch.

Harry didn't quarrel. The sun was hot, the race

was young, he was patient. He was soon lost in the dust behind me but there was no other front runner in sight. As I came around to the grandstand lane again, I saw Tom Hayworth heading for the pits and Arnie Terring just disappearing into the first turn. Tyler, Petrini and Mayer were still ahead of him and I hoped my board would tell me how far away they were.

I read the news two laps later. Mayer was leading the parade and he was three-quarters of a mile in front of me.

Three-quarters of a mile wasn't too big a lead to overcome in all the laps that were left, but it was Gus Mayer who was holding it and Gus was not a man to burn himself out in the early running. It was logical to guess Petrini and Tyler weren't far behind him and that they were also traveling at a speed they knew they could maintain. It was time to move up into their world.

I wasn't the only driver who realized the four in front were running away; Dutch Krueger came into sight behind, challenging Shaw, as I took off after Terring. It was the start of a mass movement. Everybody was waking up at the same time.

By the time I caught Terring, Krueger was riding my deck. I had been trying to avoid three-car tangles all season but there was no way of avoiding this one unless I wanted to drop back to sixth place. I concentrated on the man in front of me.

I made my move in the middle of the backstretch, trusting the Nowak's traction to carry me through the turn if Arnie stayed stubborn. He didn't back off, we charged the third turn nose to nose and logging.

Either I had played the turn wrong or I hit a soft spot that I had overlooked before. Whatever the reason, the Nowak started her slide early as I gave Arnie clearance for his. The Nowak started to slide —and wouldn't quit.

I could hear the fans in the distance yelling, the tires shrieking. I could see the fence looming as we slued up the bank. For a frightened fraction of a second, I was certain this was going to be my personal checkered flag.

But then those ridged tires found solid ground. I could feel them bite as the deck steadied and the nose swung back to normal. We headed back into the competition.

But Krueger had gone past below and so had Harry Shaw. In my badly timed bid for fourth place, I had dropped to seventh.

And the mass movement from behind kept coming and I was still a little rattled from that unexpected slide. Krueger and Shaw moved out of range. Mike Kaprelian pulled next to me in the front lane.

Seventh place was low enough, I decided, for a Duncan-readied Nowak. I had the lead and the slot into the turn and I used them both. Mike ate my dust for three hot laps and then dropped back to wait for a better time.

I didn't slow up. I had caught a glimpse of Dutch Krueger in the haze ahead. The lady continued to fly, eating the gap to Krueger. I came up behind him in turn three and could tell by the cloud of dust in front of him that there were other cars not too far ahead.

Dutch gave me more trouble than Mike had but that was to be expected. Dutch still had hopes of finishing high in the point race. I dogged him, watching his lines, trying to estimate his traction. I dogged him for a lap and a half and edged even in turn one.

He started to climb about a third of the way through the turn. I was still gun shy from my close call; I dropped back. It had been purely a safety (almost chicken) move but from the stands it must have looked strategic. Because Dutch kept climbing and the groove was mine and the Nowak was ready.

I bottomed and she responded and we were back in sixth place, only one spot lower than where we had started the race. And only a few hundred feet ahead, Shaw and Terring were pacing it out for fourth place. I kept them in sight as they seesawed, first one and then the other temporarily holding the edge.

Dutch Krueger hadn't called it quits. He kept me

conscious of his presence as I played spectator to the Terring-Shaw duel. Dutch, I guessed, was playing it as I was, waiting for more open track before he would make his bid. I was sure he didn't plan to finish this race behind Mark Devlin. There was plenty of time.

I was, my board informed me, still three-quarters of a lap behind the leader. But the new leader was Tudi Petrini. The champ was adjusting his race to the field, waiting for pretenders to his throne.

And far behind him, we played our own waiting game, Dutch and I, waiting for Terring and Shaw to resolve their battle. The laps spun on and my impatience grew and so did the ache between my shoulder blades. The air I breathed, filtered by the handkerchief, was beginning to taste gritty. I remembered how I had told Al that the sixty-five miles last week had been a breeze. This was no breeze and the race was only half over.

The Nowak whimpered impatiently. Krueger began to close in from behind. I kept the pace, fighting my own impatience, choosing the slot carefully every time we hit the third turn, my memory of that near disaster still strong in my mind.

The board informed me I was now a half-lap behind the leader, the same leader, the king. And in the sixty-second lap, Arnie Terring gave the fans a delayed replay of my earlier fence-scraper.

He played it as I had, starting his move in the

150

middle of the backstretch. Shaw had the lead and the choice of slots; the one Arnie chose was the one he considered second best, just as I had. His D-O went sliding up the bank—and I bottomed.

He was still climbing when I went by, Dutch trailing me. I kept my eyes to the front but my ears waited for a sound from behind, the sound of crashing timber.

There was none, and I began to breathe again—as Krueger appeared to my right, making his bid, hoping to get by before I could pull out to take Shaw.

That was his hope, I'm sure, but I had just spent too many weary laps as a victim of other men's strategies. I kept the heat on, gained the legal clearance—and went out after Harry Shaw.

Shaw had gone through a tiring duel with Terring; it may have been that. Or it may have been the released impatience of that soaring Nowak. We streaked past in plenty of time to choose our own line into the turn. We rode proudly into fourth place.

And as we came broadsiding into the backstretch, there was a dot ahead just disappearing around the third turn, a yellow dot, the D-O of Chris Tyler.

Petrini, Mayer and Tyler, super-star, star and apprentice star—these were the three ahead and the nearest was Tyler.

He was not loafing. I sent the lady up into her falsetto range and the threats from behind kept diminishing with every lap. But the dot ahead stayed stubbornly small. It was like the shining charm of a hypnotist, that bright yellow dot; the grit in my mouth and the ache between my shoulder blades were forgotten as the lady and I crowded the precarious rim of her tractional limit.

The dot began to grow larger, to take shape, to build hope. In the backstretch of the eighty-sixth mile I was finally close enough to challenge. But I didn't, not going into that third turn. I had learned that much today. I kept out of his heavy dust but in the striking zone.

I was glad I did. There was a tail-ender in the dust of the turn, a limping car I hadn't seen as we'd spanned the backstretch. Chris must have been aware of him but not aware of how slowly the car was traveling.

He braked and went high; I had traction enough to stay above the laggard and below Chris. We came out of the turn nose to nose, the Nowak and the yellow D-O, as the roar from the stands drowned out the scream of our engines, dead even into the grandstand lane.

I didn't need the touch; the Nowak had all the leverage I needed under the hood. We shrieked past the pits into third place, in front and gaining, the choice of first turn slots ours, the groove ours, the tougher problems of strategy Mr. Chris Tyler's.

It didn't seem to be a choice that dismayed him. He didn't pack up and go home. He stayed about four inches from my right rear wheel and I began to taste the grit in my mouth again. He had beaten himself last Sunday; I would have to beat him today.

I don't suppose I did, really. I suppose the lady did it, and Al's wrench and Al's cunning. But I don't want to be too modest; I managed to build the four inches to eight and the eight inches to a foot through that turn. In five laps, I built those four inches up to fifty feet.

There were nine miles to the checkered flag and I had picked up ten feet a lap. In a few more laps, if the percentage held, my lead would be fairly safe, barring the unexpected.

Ninety-nine percent of my brain was concentrated on staying in front, on proving my point, on staying alive and functioning. It was that sneaky little one percent that kept bouncing around in my light head.

Why are you here, Mark Devlin? Who had asked me that? Not an outsider. I was asking me that. Hadn't I answered it myself in Al's office Tuesday afternoon? We weren't here to impress Gaskin and Nowak—we were here to win, to do our best, to have fun.

Ahead, Gus Mayer did not seem to be moving at a speed beyond my reach. He went wide to lap Red Nelsen and I swung wide to follow him past. When Gus regained the groove I realized he was running below his peak and I could smell the taint of oil in his exhaust fumes. I tailed him into the south turn and took him without a struggle in the backstretch.

I knew then he wasn't peaking, because Petrini wasn't in sight. When Gus's mount was right there wasn't this much daylight between him and Petrini.

There was a dust cloud in the turn that could have been the king and when I came past our pit the board confirmed it.

"2—3—¼" was what the chalk informed me. I was second, one quarter of a lap behind the car with the big "3" on its deck, the hot Offy of Tudi Petrini.

There would be a proud "1" on that deck next season, emblematic of the championship he had already won. And proud was the definitive word. Despite his already won championship, Tudi Petrini would neither ask for nor give any quarter this final Sunday afternoon.

America, this way up—that's what I told myself. *Get ready, Mr. Petrini, because I'm climbing the stairs.*

Oh, he was ready! As a matter of fact, I think he was glad to see me. Gus's engine problems had robbed the king of a worthy foe in his final show of the season in front of his many fans.

I had watched him all summer, trying to find a flaw in his technique, a vulnerability. I had found none. *It doesn't really matter,* I thought. *I'm not here to beat his weakness; I'm here to beat his strength.*

There was no complaint from the lady. She, too, was here to win. We went up to within one zillionth of one degree of her traction limit and began to crowd Petrini.

He was all out but we stayed close. That was my whole strategy, I told myself, to stay close. If we could hang in there right up to turn four in the last lap, the leverage would be ours. We had the engine for the stretch dash to the flag.

My board no longer told me who was leading. I could see him plainly enough. But I was surprised to learn, in the ninety-eighth lap, that Chris Tyler wasn't losing any ground behind. That had to mean he was matching Petrini's best, because Tudi must have been traveling at the track limit. I knew he was traveling at *my* track limit.

Don't take any chances, one voice said. And the other argued, *Take Petrini!*

Well, why not? But when? Not on that third turn; I had been trailing him through that, eating his grit. And on the last turn of the race, what if he came out far enough in front to overcome my only edge, the few extra horses in the Nowak?

Then I would finish second. There should be no shame in that, finishing second to Tudi Petrini. But I didn't plan to. My strategy stayed constant—hang in close enough and trust the car that Al had worked on all summer.

It wasn't easy. He handled the turns better; I made it up in the stretches. At the start of the last lap, there was no board showing. Al and Pete knew I had problems enough in front of me; there was nothing I could do about any problems from behind.

I lost a few feet through turns one and two, came back to ride his deck in the backstretch. I missed the soft spot on turn three and the wave of sound from the stands was like a wall as we climbed the bank, trailing the king.

He had the best line out and it gave him a twelve-foot lead. But his edge of skill was behind him. From here on neither of us had anything to do with the race. Each of us could only push his right foot to the floor. The race would be won or lost by the engines in front of us.

I could see the starter ahead. I could see the whole long line of faces in the pits. The sound from the stands was like a continuous explosion, a roll of thunder, as the twelve feet dropped to ten and the ten to eight and then stayed constant at eight as the flag got bigger and my heart sank.

That was when the lady took over. I could swear she growled; I *know* she jumped. The eight feet was suddenly no feet and we were past and still flying long before the flag dropped. She had done the impossible; she had taken the great Petrini.

It was quite a future, the way Stan Nowak explained it. I would be on salary as a member of the pit crew until I was old enough and ready for the USAC. From then on, it would be salary and per-

156

centage and he had Roy Gaskin explain to me what *that* had meant to *him*.

I could see Gaskin's big Lincoln in the background as they talked. I could see Al and Pete, loading the lady, minding their own business. In my mind, I could see Larry Beam. The kind of money Mr. Nowak was talking about—well, maybe I could start another bank and give Larry's dad some competition.

It was a bright picture they were painting. But when they were finished, I said politely, "I'm sorry. It's not for me. Thank you, just the same."

Gaskin stared and Nowak frowned. And Stan Nowak said, "I can make it sweeter. I don't mind telling you I'm sold on you, son."

"It isn't the money," I explained. "You couldn't sweeten it enough. There isn't that much money, Mr. Nowak."

He had a patient (if puzzled) look on his face now. His voice was calm. "Okay. It's your decision. But would you tell an old man why?"

"It's simple enough," I told him. "I don't want to leave my friends."

And they left, to talk to Chris, I suppose, though I had a hunch about him. I think he liked it here, too. It didn't matter; there'd be enough competition in the WDTA next year with or without Chris Tyler.

I went over to help my friends get the lady loaded for the ride home.